WIREBOOK V

by

PRESS JONES
N8UG

Published by:
The Wireman, Inc
261 Pittman Road
Landrum, SC 29356

We Remember

L B CEBIK
W4RNL

A good friend deeply dedicated to Amateur Radio, and a mentor in the publishing of **WIREBOOK IV** in 2004. LB's skills in the technical aspects of wire antennas are hidden in the simplicity of what we offer in loops and dipoles, but you'll profit be his work, and his skills are still available since he became an SK on his great website, <www.cebik.com>

I am proud to have been a TA for the AARL along with LB for a number of years. Many times, when I had no answer as to "why," a call to LB was all that was needed for the amateur, skilled or simply curious, to fill the gaps.

After some 4,000 copies, we finally sold out **WBIV** and began to put **WBV** together, and with help from LB and many others.

LB also studied many other amateur devices and was near publishing some balun material on samples submitted by the Wireman, now available to the amateur family

LB – W4RNL became a Silent Key on April 22, 2008

He is deeply missed.

Acknowledgements

Thanks, Deborah, for your patience, prodding and encouragement toward getting the book to this point, all as you did practically everything at The Wireman, Inc (still). while I pecked away at the computer.

Thanks, daughter Brenda, for the sketches and drawings scattered throughout the book.

Thanks, Vic Du Bois, wherever you are, for the great cartoons!

Thanks, Walt, W2DU, for the continuing tutelage and encouragement in the mysteries of baluns.

Thanks for tips, help, and ideas from W1ICP(SK), K1PEK, W1RFI, K1VDZ, K1YPP, W2FMI, W3JI, WB4A(SK), W4RNL(SK), WX4TM, KR4Y M(SK), W7EL, KC7RK, W8JI, W8TBP(SK), WA8UAN(SK), W8UR R(SK), W9DNI, WA5FRF, AD4FI, W7RF, W6NKT, W4JYL

and

Thanks to the countless numbers of friends and amateurs with whom I've shared the amateur radio experience for 35 years. There's a bit of all of you in **The Wireman!**

Welcome to WIREBOOK V

There has been a lot of water over the dam since Wirebook IV, but the reasons for the Wirebooks remain the same: to make the experience of Amateur Radio a greater pleasure in practice through either hands-on activity or understanding more about it. WB V is the same as WB IV plus a lot more detailed procedures, new hints, ideas, and testimonials from hams who built great wire antennas.

There is a lot more to acquiring wire and cable, amateur equipment and accessories than, for example, buying a TV or stereo, plugging it in, and hooking it up to cable or an antenna. Many amateurs will spend a bundle for a nice piece of equipment, hook it up to the old CB feed line or worse, and then wonder why it doesn't work properly.

When all else fails, "read the directions," This means somewhat more than the manual, since the manufacturer is more inclined to give you the straight dope on the equipment than on the details of anything beyond the basic hookup. "Read the directions," means more than the study of the manual and the material required to obtain an amateur license, since learning basic theory does not necessarily bring one up to date with the state of the art. There are a lot of great books, manuals, and periodicals out there – use them!

Another favorite source of knowledge is your fellow amateur. The hobby could not and will not survive without the flow and exchange of information among its participants, but as the case with any subject, the listener must sort out what he hears before accepting any of it as gospel. Many amateurs think anyone in the world with a call sign knows all the answers, and they will practice blind loyalty to "good old Elmer." This can be OK, and usually is, but it doesn't guarantee that your "Elmer" hasn't been making the same mistakes for many years, and hasn't read article one about where technology is today.

Today's radio amateur is strongly urged to "do his homework" before making any purchase. Compare notes, check up on all advice, get several opinions, and blow out the well-meaning "chaff." It's your money and you should get the most for it. Too often an amateur will tell a supplier, "I don't know which cable (or whatever) to buy. Fix me up so I can get on the air." This approach can, with a good supplier, get one the right material, but it can also lead to overkill and a waste of money or a serious error.

There is a human tendency, the seeds of which are in all of us, that says, "If a little is good, then a lot must be better." This concept leads to trying to solve a problem by throwing money at it, which very seldom works. Our experience shows that nearly half of those asking us for advice receive a recommendation for a lower cost item than they thought was needed.

The **Wirebook** is a collection of information gathered as a consequence of thousands of conversations at hamfests, on the phone, and from discussions with authors, researchers, "tech-reps," engineers, and quality control people. The information was gathered simply because it was necessary for us to answer the myriad of questions directed to us from all quarters of the amateur community.

After 35 years of fielding questions in the amateur community, we've accumulated a lot of answers. We've learned that amateur radio people are among the most curious on the planet and that their thirst for knowledge in the field is insatiable. Compiling the collection of answers we've garnered and making them available to whomever needs them is what the **Wirebook** is all about. We hope that you use it along with other sources to get the most satisfaction and pleasure from our great hobby. This edition is larger than **WB IV** for several reasons: Many readers have requested a larger type, and we're happy to comply again, since yours truly has the same need! Secondly, the content, by specific request, and the depth of the new and repetitive subject matter in our tech support, has expanded three-fold.

We hope you find **WIREBOOK V** useful!

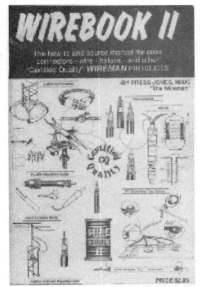

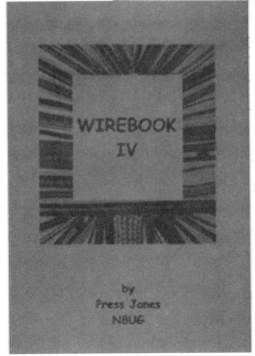

Memories!

Table of Contents

Chapter 1 Communication
Hams Talk, But Do They Communicate?

10-13

You clearly said,
"We would both share in the joy of our hobbies!"

Hams Talk - But Do They Communicate?

"I want a hundred feet of your best coax"
"How do you plan to use it?"
"For amateur radio"
"OK, swell. But................"

We're constantly in awe at the way our loquacious friends in the hobby talk with complete abandon, but very often fail to communicate.

The other day, seeking tech support on a problem with my AT&T server on the web, I was directed to a series of questions concerning my system, hardware, software, etc., etc., to the point that, irritated, I began to wonder what they wanted next – my shirt and pants size? What kind of car do I drive? I subdued my feelings and plugged along, at least it was better than waiting for a technician on the phone after pressing 1, 2, 3, 4, to get to the point where I could listen to a robot tell me that the whole darn crew was busy helping others, and to please hang in there.

It got me to thinking, though, and brought back a definition laid on me by at least one teacher many years ago for the "Scientific Method:"

"Principles and procedures for the systematic pursuit of knowledge involving the recognition and formulation of a problem, the collection of data through observation and experiment, and the formulation and testing of hypotheses"

Sounds kind of heavy, I'll admit, so let's try this: **Got a problem? Gather all of the information on every facet of it and the solution will present itself.**

AT&T's questions on the web say just this: *solutions are impossible without the facts, man!* Sure, a lot of the questions are probably superfluous, but that is not known until the solution is at hand. In fact, I talked to a tech rep as well, and his protocol was the same. It was a hefty batch of questions followed by a short pause. While the line was silent, he plugged in all of the data, and his computer laid out a solution, which he then used to talk me through the repair. Surely, you didn't think every helpful technician had all of the answers in his head, did you? Let's face it. If he did, he wouldn't be working the 3rd shift tech support helping computer illiterates like me!

So what's my point?

Simple. When you spend hundreds, even thousands of dollars on the amateur radio station of your dreams, you either know what you are doing, or you take the word of the company that put it all together. Or, perhaps it's the coolest rig in the catalog, or maybe it's the one your "Elmer" has! Then, to connect your pride and joy to the antenna and ground, the correct RF and control cables and wires are required, and no vendor knows what you need until you tell him. Also, if you don't know, you either have to learn what to tell, or find an expert who, with the data from you, can spell out the "right stuff" for you.

Sometimes, even reading the directions helps!

The stream of data that will produce the right answers includes, at the very least the following: all of the operating frequencies, the power used on each, the characteristics of the route from shack to antenna, the type of antenna(s) and whether stationary or rotated, the type of tower (fixed, crank-up, etc.), if any. The operating style (casual, "rag chew," QRP, DX'r, Super DX'r, contester, experimenter, or "traffic specialist,") are all data needed for the right choice, not to mention special circumstances such as a budget!

Know what you have, learn what's available, decide what you need, and specify it, and please don't call your vendor and say only, "Send me some RG8." Even worse, don't surf the web and pick the biggest and the best, "just cuz!" Don't be afraid to pump the dealer. It's his job to know the best answers for your situation, and if he doesn't, he should either find out or direct you.

As you might suspect, most of the information we offer in the **Wirebook** is based on the many questions we try to answer in the course of doing business in the amateur community. Many times we don't know the answer either, but we almost always know where to find it. Our best sources must have the details, just like a doctor or a detective, in order to offer a good answer or piece of advice, so we prepare a check list before asking. He's not a mind reader.

Here, for example, are some things I'd like to know before recommending a type of feed line or antenna wire:

Frequency(s), Power, and Mode
Approximate length and route in detail of antenna and feedline you have in mind
Tower,if any, and/or crank-up, etc.
Pole, tree, attic, etc.
Primary operating style
Loss tolerance
Cost range
Unusual circumstances
Shoe size-----oops, wrong list!

Now I would love to talk you into the simplest, cheapest, and easiest antenna and feedline possible, from which you would have great results and learn the most by doing and using, not by spending a fortune for a "plug and play" setup!

The following pages encourage you to "**gather all of the information...**" and then communicate well in the greatest hobby of all, which, by the way, is all about communication!

Grand-dad used to tell us about his neighbor on the farm in North Carolina who dropped by to ask for advice but had difficulty getting to the point. Grampa said, "He'd just start talking and keep on talking until he thought of something to say!"

I'm sure I've had a QSO with one of that neighbor's progeny on 80 meters!

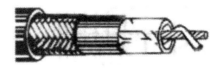

Coaxial Cable Design and Construction

Coaxial cable n (1936): a transmission line that consists of a tube of electrically conductive material surrounding a central conductor held in place by insulators and that is used to transmit telegraph, telephone, and television signals of high frequency -- also called **Coax**[1]

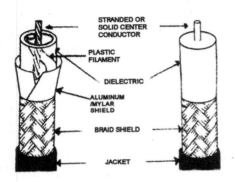

The definition is simple, but the "how" is important. Unless the center conductor is dead center throughout 100% of the length and the OD (outside diameter) of the center conductor, and both the ID (inside diameter) and OD of the outer conductor are constant, the RF (radio frequency) performance of the cable will be impaired. These dimensions also determine, in great part, the power handling capability, the loss characteristics, and the characteristic impedance of the cable.

Looking first at the center conductor, we find solid (one strand, wire, or end) or multi-strand bare copper (bc), copper-clad steel (ccs), copper-clad aluminum (ccal), tinned copper (tc), tinned copper-clad steel (tccs), silvered copper (sc), or silvered copper-clad steel (sccs), to mention a few.

The best RF propagation is over the surface (remember skin effect?) of a solid conductor. Silver plating can be a further enhancement. This becomes more significant as frequency increases, but only as one of the determining factors. Solid or single strand center conductors are used where a minimum of flexing will be required beyond that required during installation.

Stranded wire is much easier to use and will last longer without distortion or fracture under continuous flexing. The greater RF resistance than that of a solid conductor can be minimized by design. The number of strands depends on the degree of flexibility required. The more strands, the tighter

---

[1]Merriam-Webster's Collegiate® dictionary, 10th ed.

the lay[2] and compression,[3] the more the stranded conductor coax emulates the propagation of solid wire. The difference can be reduced to practically zero at low frequencies but becomes wider as signal wavelength shortens. (See more discussion of this phenomenon under **"Antenna Wire."**)

The center conductor is surrounded by a dielectric material that consists of air, plastic, ceramic or other material, all of which attempt to get as close to dry or no air as possible within the structural limitations of the design of the cable. This is an extrusion process, either directly onto the wire or as a continuous extrusion of a tube over a wire enclosed by a spiral of polyethylene. Solid polyethylene is the most common material, followed by foamed polyethylene with widely different solids percentages. Solid or foamed Teflon™ is prevalent in higher temperature applications, and many other types of plastic are used in specialized constructions. The term "semi-solid" polyethylene (or Teflon®) describes a system, which includes a spiral plastic filament supporting the center conductor in the center of a plastic tube. Other terms that describe this style are **ASP** or **AST**, short for "**A**ir **S**paced **P**olyethylene" or "**A**ir **S**paced **T**eflon®". This dielectric style, properly applied and maintained, provides one of the lowest-loss constructions possible, albeit subject to problems unique to its style. Dielectric material performs the basic function of precisely supporting the center conductor, and becomes a major factor in the determination of the characteristic impedance and the loss characteristics based on its formula and density. The measured values are mainly the **Capacitance** and **Velocity Factor** or **Velocity of Propagation**.

Velocity of propagation (VP) is the speed of a radio frequency signal, which in free space or a total vacuum is the same as the speed of light. In the atmosphere or other me-

---

[2] "Lay" is the linear distance from where strand #1 exactly ends one 360-degree spiral path along the multi-strand wire.

[3] Compression refers to a pass of the wire after stranding through a die to shape the product cylindrically and adjust the final diameter if required.

dium such as gas, coaxial cable dielectric, enamel coatings, etc., the signal is slowed down by an amount specific to the material involved. The **Velocity Factor (VF)** is the ratio of the lesser speed to the speed of light, expressed as a decimal or percent. For example, open wire transmission line **VF** is 91 to 95%, while solid polyethylene coaxial cable dielectric **VF** is 66%. Solid Teflon's®[4] **VF** is typically 69.5%, while most foams are 78%. The new state-of-the-art foams have **VF**'s of up to 89%. In general, the higher the **VF**, the lower the loss in/on an RF conductor, making it an important criteria in cable design.

Capacitance is measured in picofarads (**pf**) per foot between center conductor and shield, and this, along with the size of the cable elements and the value of the **VF**, determines the characteristic impedance.

Shield employs one or more of a variety of materials including aluminum Mylar® foil, tinned or bare copper braid, spiral served fine wire, and copper or aluminum tube. It provides an RF shield as well as a return path.

The percentage of coverage is logically considered as you would measure optical shielding. That is, the percentage closed to the passage of light and, therefore, RF. The percentage of shielding is related to design[5], not quality. The higher the frequency, the shorter the wavelength, therefore the higher percentage of shielding required for minimal RF leakage. In amateur usage, 95% bare or tinned single copper braid shield is more than adequate for all HF work and most 6 and 2 meter operation. Foil[6] plus 95% tinned copper braid is best for critical 2 meters and all VHF and UHF. The foil shield under braid contributes to the lower loss capability for the same reasons discussed earlier for stranded versus solid conductors.

The foil/plastic laminate, if used, is applied just as the coax "core" enters the braider, as a ribbon, guided and

---

[4] Dupont trademark, used as a general term for PTFE and FEP, for simplicity.

[5] Braid factor is determined based on wire size, count and cable size.

[6] "Foil" refers to any number of combinations of Mylar® or similar plastic and aluminum placed between braid and dielectric as a 100% extra shield, though not necessarily a conductor.

formed around the core in lineal fashion, overlapped or fluted and seamed. The braid is then applied just like braided rope is made – "maypole style" – except that instead of a couple dozen happy kids, it would take, in one example, 24 groups of 8 kids each roaring around, in and out, with a wire in hand to cover the pole! There is more space filled by braiders in a wire plant than any other mechanical part of the process.

Some of the low-loss coaxes feature "bonded foil," wherein the foil/plastic laminate is bonded to the dielectric. This is accomplished by heating the cable as it emerges from the braider, just enough to fuse the laminate to the dielectric.

Double (or more) braid shields, an example of which is made with silvered copper wire such as in RG214/U, supplies as much as 98% shielding, and have been used for years in repeater interconnections between cavities, duplexers, and separate transmitter and receiver setups up through 220 MHz, beyond which 100% shield is preferred. The foil/braid combinations in coax or the continuous metal wall of "**hard line**" meet this requirement.

Jacket, the outside of the coax, consists of another wide variety of compounds. The most common is Polyvinyl chloride (PVC), which comes in many different formulations. The basic PVC is known under MILITARY SPECIFICATIONS as **Class I**. It has a useful life of 5 to 10 years, has generally good qualities across the board, and is economical. An example is RG58/U.

Class IIA is also PVC but is referred to as "non-contaminating." The term applies to the chemical makeup of the plastic, making it less reactive to the other plastics in the cable for a net result of greater longevity for all reasons, including, but not limited to, ultra violet resistance. Under similar environments to that of Class I, Class IIA should last 10 to 15 years. *"Non-contaminating" does **not** mean, "**designed for direct burial**," no matter what you may have read in the periodicals or even handbooks. To an amateur, it simply means that no matter what the application, compared with Class I, it will last longer,- period.* Examples include RG58C/U, **honest** RG213/U, and most CQ 4XL cables.

A note of caution in regard to Class I and II coaxes: *Where multiple runs of coax are bundled or lay together in a pipe, the classes should not be mixed, since the plasticizers in Class I material will adversely affect both Class I and II types, i.e. the lifespan of Class II tends to revert to that of Class I.*

Class IIIA refers to black polyethylene jacket, used where greater moisture resistance, ultra violet and abrasion resistance is required. It is found as the outer jacket on most direct bury-type cables, and its useful life can exceed 20 years. *A polyethylene jacket alone does not define a direct bury cable, but it is widely used for that purpose alone or with water-blocking compounds, armor, and all-metal shielding for different levels of performance.* Example: **CQ Direct Burial RG213/U, p/n CQ113PE, with PE and water-block.**

Class V is fiberglass braid, usually over Teflon™ such as in RG141/U.

Class VII is usually Teflon® tape, wrapped, as in RG188/U.

Class IX is extruded Teflon®, most impervious to weather, chemically inert, and heat resistant to 200 degrees C and more. (Also the most expensive!) Examples are RG142B/U and RG303/U. Classes V, VII, and IX are often defined as "plenum" types, allowing them to be used within heating ducting and fire risk areas.

Hard Line describes coaxial cable with a solid metal outer shield, usually made from aluminum or copper, either smooth or corrugated. Both are made with 50 and/or 75-ohm characteristic impedance in many sizes and configurations. They are the most permanent, lowest loss, and trouble-free installations. They are expensive, but economical commercially and necessary in our hi-tech age. "Big Gun" and bargain hunting amateurs often employ new and surplus hard line in many contest and QRP stations.

Hard Line is manufactured in much the same way as coax, up to the application of the shield. Two methods of applying the metallic outer conductor are of interest. An early method still used for some work involves sliding a long core (center conductor and main dielectric) into a long extruded tube of copper or aluminum. The composite then passes through a die that compresses the tube onto the core, and the complete cable is then jacketed if required. This is a batch process, limited by the length of metal extrusion possible. A continuous process involves the same approach with a ribbon of metal instead of a tube. The metal is rolled or shaped into a tube around the core and the seam is continuously welded. Rapid cooling of the finished product precludes damage to the core, and a further rolling or drawing process usually follows. Flexibility in "hard line" is added by corrugation of the tube, but such flexibility is designed mainly for installation purposes since the number of bends before metal fracture is limited.

This is basic wire and cable construction. The miles of material produced annually are similar in principal, but every manufacturer has a "better way," at least in *his* facility. The search is never-ending for the ultimate transmission line, and the amateur community continues to contribute to the art. We are able to try any new idea without the regulatory restrictions of the commercial market, and new products continue to be born of this process.

Coaxial Cable –
Quality - "Mil Spec" - Choices

This article, published in all prior WIREBOOKS, has been so well received over the years that it must be a part of WIREBOOK V. The author has edited, added to, and updated the content. It is, after all, an ever developing subject, so at least skim it, dear reader, even if you've "been there, done that!"

There is a lot of good product out there and some not so good. Unfortunately, the stuff that is in the "almost as good as" category is always there, simply because there is plenty of money to be made with it from uninformed buyers. The smart customer is the well-informed customer.

Coaxial cable listings employ private, commercial and **RG** designations and descriptions.

What's an "RG?"

Cables used at radio frequencies and manufactured for the government in this country have been identified and classified with the **"RG"** legend since the 1940's.

R = RADIO FREQUENCY
G = GOVERNMENT
  8 = an example of the sequential number assigned to
      the government approval, thus, RG8/U.
U = UNIVERSAL SPECIFICATION

The **RG** terminology is now all but obsolete in industry, but it still provides one convenient means of getting at least close to what one needs for a specific project as long as catalogs and references still list it.

One must be careful, however, since the terminology is neither always specific nor up to date. For example, the popular description, **RG8/U** no longer pins down size, capacitance, shielding, stranding, dielectric, plating, metal, or jacketing. It only *indicates* a coaxial cable of nominal 50 ohm characteristic impedance with an outside diameter of about 0.405."

Tradition and non-current references generate calls most every day, asking simply, "How much is your **RG8**?" Any kind of honest answer would require a listing of specifications in addition to the parameters above, and anything less could result in an expensive mistake.

What is MIL SPEC?

MIL SPEC is a term used to tell one that *"if there is a military specification for the item, this product is made to meet the specifications and tolerances cited therein."* When the item is made for the government or under government contract, it is subject to detailed inspection during manufacture and as finished product prior to acceptance to earn a **QPL** (Qualified Product Listing). As you might expect, cable purchased that satisfies these standards would cost as much as twice what you will see in our, or anyone else's, price list.

A few years ago, it became illegal to call it "Mil Spec" unless it really was, so the terms **"MIL TYPE"** or **"MIL SPEC TYPE"** were coined. This means, or at least implies that the cable is **RG** classifiable and is made to specs that adhere to **RG** standards where applicable. In other words, if the manufacturer is one who has a reputation for high quality and does not practice "*commercial double-speak*," it is reasonable to assume that cable so designated is some of his best product.

On the other hand, if the manufacturer and/or distributor are something less than top quality-minded, and profit is the over-riding motivation; there is nothing to stop him from using the same terminology. Sounds like the old story, doesn't it? "*Let the buyer beware*" is as true as it has ever been, and the amateur who doesn't do his homework is apt to waste his money and degrade his station's performance.

So far we've been able to follow the **KISS**[7] rule here, but two factors still cloud the issue:

First, there are literally hundreds of excellent coaxial cables in the market place and under private and commercial contract that have very little resemblance to anything in the **RG** category, and second, the **RG** designations themselves are rapidly disappearing from the industry reference material.

Back in the 1940's, **Mil-C-17** became the government specification document standardizing coaxial cables. In the 70's, M17 numbers replaced the RG term, but few of us outside of the government and government contractors had any reason to notice. Revisions abound, and **MIL-C-17** is now revision **G**; the criteria have narrowed, and all **M17** numbers are **QPL**.

---

[7] "Keep It Simple, Stupid."

For all practical purposes, the coaxial cables in the amateur community are completely outside of the **MIL-C-17** realm, the only exceptions being that which "slides" out of the military base in the trunk of the car or appears at swap shops and flea markets from military surplus, vintage 10-25 or more years. The value of **MIL-C-17** to us, then, is as a marvelous source of information and learning as we design, build, compare, and operate in the RF world, hobby or avocation.

We will probably continue to use **RG** numbers for years as a means to describe size and impedance. The following descriptions are provided to "get a feel" for the basic classes from which most amateur needs are met.

The RG58 Type At or near 0.195 inches OD (outside diameter) and 50 to 53.5 ohms characteristic impedance. The most popular versions have 95% braid shield, solid polyethylene dielectric, and PVC (polyvinyl chloride) jackets. The center conductor of **RG58/U** is solid 20 AWG bare copper. **RG58A/U** and **RG58C/U** are both 20AWG stranded tinned copper. **RG 58C/U** also has the Class IIA or non-contaminating jacket. All three are **MIL SPEC** type.

RG58/U is popular for bargain transmission lines at HF, computer networking, and coaxial dipoles (see also CQ**124**, specially made for coaxial dipoles and bazookas). The very flexible **RG 58A/U** is most popular for short transmission lines for mobile HF and VHF, as is **RG 58C/U** for the same reasons plus the longer life of its Class IIA non-contaminating jacket. (See page 37 for examples)

In recent years, a number of new versions of **RG58**-type cables have appeared, driven by the need for lower loss and greater shielding at UHF (trunking business systems, cellular, computer networking, etc). The new arrivals have offered higher performance, with 10%, to as much as 40% less loss and 100% shielding due to foil plus braid shield and hi-tech foam dielectric. **(CQ129FF), LMR 200 and others**

At distances up to 100 feet, an RG58-type coax will make a fine transmission line for HF stations as well as jumpers, etc. within the shack unless you are a "dyed in the wool" DX'er or QRP'er.

Many 8X's. It is for every type of station. 0.242" OD, 50-ohm characteristic impedance. **RG8X** is actually a misnomer since it was never so designated. "**8X, MINI 8, MICRO 8**," etc., are all aliases for this popular coax which falls between the RG58's and RG8's. It has a safe power limit of about 700 watts at HF due to the lower melting point of its foam polyethylene dielectric. The better quality versions have about 95% bare copper braid shield, 16 AWG stranded bare copper center conductor, and a Class I PVC jacket. There are also several low-loss types as well as Class IIA and polyethylene-jacketed models.

Used with proper care, **8X** is a great cable – light and very flexible, easy to use, and 10 to 15% less loss than the RG58's, a real plus at 30 to 300 MHz. This class of coax is very popular for HF and shorter VHF feed lines, mobile and marine jumpers, etc., and has a basic cost just a bit higher than the RG58's. Here again great strides have been made recently. There are now a whole group of **8X's**, to cover a major portion of an amateur or professional station's needs economically(See page 37 for examples). Like RG58, there are several dual shield models such as **CQ118**, with 19 strand center conductor, and **LMR 240UF**, with 7 strand centerconductor.

Versatile RG8/RG213U types are a step up in physical size and power-handling capability. The old **RG8A/U**, now **MIL SPEC RG213/U** or its equivalent, is the workhorse of the HF bands and still the most popular. It is also overkill for many of the applications for which it is chosen. (The amateur, "...if a little is good, a lot must be better, ...syndrome!")

Top quality **RG213/U** has a Class IIA non-contaminating jacket, 95-97% bare copper braid shield, solid polyethylene dielectric, and a 13 AWG, 7 strand bare copper center conductor. It will handle 3500 watts at HF (10 MHz) for the full power station, the heavy DX'er, and, with less loss than most **8X**, it is great for QRP. At 2 meters, it will do well up to 100 feet for anything less than DX work.

There is a lot of **RG213/U** on the market. Look for a brand name you are comfortable with, and terms such as **MIL SPEC, MIL SPEC TYPE, ENHANCED MIL SPEC**, etc. on the cable, not just in the advertisements. Unfortunately there are no limits to the claims made in labeling, so, in many cases, it just "ain't so." (See page 2.24 for examples that follow the rules!)

Foam dielectric — good or bad?

Foamed dielectric is used in all sizes of coax. This was a big deal back in the CB boom period when varieties of RG8 and 8X were offered as a "super low-loss coax." This was mostly hype, since the signal loss improvement at 11 meters was on the order of 0.10 dB or so, unreadable on most any meter!

In fact, foam dielectric was highly subject to moisture contamination, shorter lived, easily crushable, and usually more expensive. On the positive side, it was lighter, easier to work with, and economical. Commercially, it required nearly half the polyethylene for the dielectric, so it helped with the war effort and made a lot more money for the manufacturer.

Foamed dielectrics have come a long way since the early days, and the best of them have none of the disadvantages above. Indeed, the *lowest loss, longest-lived coaxial cables in the world today, are foamed.* There is no reason not to use a high quality foam dielectric coaxial cable simply because of a bad memory of an earlier, poorer product. Proper installation techniques, however, are still as important as ever.

Moving along from most HF applications to very long runs (200-300 feet or more) at HF to VHF and up, the next step up in cost and down in loss is the coaxial cable dubbed the "**Poor Man's Hardline**," first made famous in the amateur community as the significant upgrade to by **The Wireman, Inc.** with the 1987 innovation, "**Flexi-4XL" Wireman CQ102.**

The early **PMH** products **(CQ 101, CQ102), CQ106 "Super 8"** have, remarkably, more than 40% less loss than **RG213/U**, all with stranded center conductor, and **CQ1000 and LMR 400** with solid center conductor They have 100% shielding, and cost as little as 1/4 the price of hard line of net comparable performance. They have a tough polyethylene jacket for long life, 95% tinned copper braid for structural and electrical capability and positive connector security, aluminum Mylar™ foil shield, air or foam dielectric, and large solid or stranded bare copper center conductor.

The "care and feeding" of the **PMH** types is detailed in a separate article in this chapter. Attention to the information therein will help to get the most out of this type of coaxial cable. It's your station – make it sing and shout!

LMR and others now make them in many sizes from 0.10 to 1.250 inches for fixed through ultra-flexible installations. Short of getting a "freebie," there is no good reason for today's amateur to use hard line instead of this material. It is the best choice for very long HF transmission lines, and all VHF/UHF work up to well over 30 GHz!

Stranded conductor versions of this new technology began with products made by **TMS** for **The Wireman** and sold as such with great initial success. Unfortunately, problems developed with the loss characteristics and the project was shelved until sometime later, when **TMS** introduced them as the **UF series in the various LMR® sizes, qualified to as much as 15% greater** loss than the solid conductor models, with fewer but larger strand sizes and thermoplastic elastomer (rubber-like) jacket.

The Wireman continued with an upgraded **"Super 8,"** **CQ106,** of similar construction but holding to a 19-strand conductor and a PVC XL jacket. It became the leader in this category in the mid 1990's and has continued to be improved even as we write. **Belden's** stranded **9913F®** emerged at about the same time with loss characteristics equaling their original **9913**. It was modeled very closely to our **CQ1001FF**, but after a few years it ran into similar loss problems and inconsistencies before being pulled off from the market.

The re-emergence of the **Belden** product as **9913F7®** and the **TMS** product as **LMR 400UF®**, both with 7 strand conductor and PE-type jacket bring the saga up to date, with **CQ106** running right along with the pack.. The advertised loss characteristics of the group place **Belden, TMS** and **The Wireman** in almost a dead heat.

Another member of the club is **"Buryflex®,"** by **Davis RF**, a fine product and "Kissin' Cousin" of **CQ106**. It differs only in its rugged polyethylene jacket, making it the best low-loss RG8-type coax on the market for high abrasion risk, crank-up towers, and in or on the ground applications.

Belden's high tech **7810A**® and related cables now rival the **LMR**® solid conductor line in performance.

Made with similar technology as **CQ 106**, are **CQ118, (8X size),** and **CQ129FF (RG58 size).** All are economy-priced equivalents or improvements based on amateur radio needs.

One additional innovation worth noting is *The Wireman's* flexible version of an old **MIL SPEC RG217/U.** Known as **p/n CQ142A**; this product carries the high power and low-loss characteristics of the true **RG217/U.** The need for a special jumper around the rotor is eliminated, and the whole feed line can replace hard line at half the cost. With the addition of a tough, 20-year PE jacket and a stranded center conductor, it is perfect for maximum amateur power installations that employ telescoping or crank-up towers and/or rotors.

This covers the current crop of coaxial cables and attempts to guide the amateur with making his choice. Please note that there has to be an inference here of, to some degree, single frequency operation in cable choice. For example, a station operating into an antenna resonant at 3.850 MHz could operate very well with an **RG58** transmission line at that frequency, plus or minus 50 KHz, up to a kilowatt; but if he chose to use a tuner and work from 3.5 to 4.0, he should be using **RG213** or more. The reason is simple – SWR. Up it goes as the antenna is tuned from its resonant point. The signals make more trips up and down the line with coincident copper loss and heat, requiring larger cable to handle the load.

Complete detail for the coaxial cables referred to so far, and many more, can be found in the table pages at the end of this chapter.

Tip: When building fractional-wave coax jumpers using solid dielectric types, arithmetic calculations of length are reasonably accurate for most amateur applications. When doing the same job with foam or ssp dielectric coax, instrument confirmation is necessary for good accuracy. Published VF data is nominal or average, and accurate only in long cable lengths. This is only partially related to quality.

Hint: Forget coax for HF and use ladder line and a tuner! More signal to the antenna than any coax for 75% less money, anywhere on all the bands! Interesting? Read the material on balanced line in Chapter 6.

Proper use of Poor Man's Hard Line

The **CQ4XL** line of coaxial cable, initiated and inspired by **Belden's 9913**® in an RG8 type size, has been an exciting phase in coax technology. **ASP** (Air-spaced polyethylene) or **SSP** (Semi-solid polyethylene) was the sensation in the 1980's and 1990's with its 40+ percent less loss and better shielding than what most of us were used to with RG8A/U and RG213/U types.

ASP or **SSP** dielectric means that the center conductor is supported in the exact center of a plastic tube by a spiral filament of polyethylene. The critical dimensions involved and the combination of air and plastic dielectric sets the characteristic impedance and, along with the foil and braid, establishes the loss characteristics.

The solid center conductor is unusual in that it is very large, up to three AWG (American Wire Gauge) units larger than the nearest RG 8 type made, and *is therefore much stiffer and require special connectors.*

The bend <u>radius</u> rule for coaxial cable (minimum radius = 15 x OD/2) is critical in this cable due to this construction, since the spiral-supported, solid center conductor, when excessively bent, will be forced off-center to some degree, violating the true coaxial design and thus changing both its characteristic impedance and loss characteristics.

Of even greater importance is repetitive bending of the solid center conductor in this type of coax (**9913).** A number of reports over the years stating that with big loops, taped bundles, etc., it works just fine, but consider this: Way back in Cub Scouts many of us learned that if you hammer or bend soft copper long enough, it gets as hard as nails and has to be annealed again to make it soft enough to work. *So, repetitively bend a soft 9.5 AWG copper conductor supported by a thin plastic spiral enough times to harden the metal and then tell me that you still have a 50 ohm coax throughout its projected life of 5 to 15 years – not!*

The obvious solution to such problems is the use of coax designed for the job, and, happily, there are now many choices in the **PMH** category. These include: **CQ Flexi-4XL** (p/n **CQ102**), **CQ106 Super 8, LMR400UF®, Belden's 9913F7®,** and a number of subsequent copycats. These coaxes have a stranded center conductor that will protect the coax from damage in a well-designed installation if the same guidelines are followed.

One of the most persistent problems encountered with the use of **ASP** cable is moisture contamination, which renders the coax useless for its intended purpose. There have even been industry recommendations not to use it outdoors and we've heard a stream of complaints that it is the cable's fault. Water can enter the above-described coax by a variety of means, *none of which are the fault of the cable design*.

An understanding of the problem's cause can be of help in its solution, and the following is offered in the interest of getting the full benefit from this unique type of cable, indoors and out:

Installation. The most obvious source of leakage is an improperly installed connector. The manufacturer's recommendations should be closely followed. We have seen no shortcuts or pet schemes that work as well as the classic methods found in the **Amphenol** and other standard directions, or as described in this book. Some of these "pet" methods are ridiculous!

Condensation. This is subtler, but no less of a real problem. Picture a coil of tubing, which is what this type of coax is, purchased at a ham fest or wherever, with both ends open and stored at home in the basement or garage in a high humidity area until used. The humid air migrates into the "tube" for a week, a month, or more. Finally our operator installs the connectors, runs the line, and carefully seals the weather end of the antenna. The seasons progress, and one crisp fall day the temperature reaches a point at which the dew point of the air within the "tube" is reached. Moisture condenses in the "tube" and the design characteristics of the cable are compromised. The conscientious amateur who sealed everything well is frustrated and furious and blames the coax.

Aspiration is the biggest offender by a country mile. The "tube" full of bone-dry air is installed on a bright sunny day with connectors applied with classic perfection. The operator uses "boots" or tape on both ends to avoid any type of moisture penetration (or sometimes forgets), and puts the station to work. A week or month or so later, after thunderstorms, the SWR goes sky high, and investigation shows water in the coax, often in a climate like that of Florida. There is a high temperature, say, 90 to 100 F, and a sudden deluge of rain. The cable is rapidly chilled by 20 to 30 degrees, creating a partial vacuum in the "tube," which, in the continuing deluge of rain, causes water to be "inhaled" along micro seam overlays in the tape or along the surface up under the boot. Sometimes, the moisture path is through the antenna's feed point connector, overlooked in the sealing process.

The avoidance of these problems is simple:

1. Keep the cable dry from the start. Store it inside the house out of the sunlight. Seal the ends by dipping the ends in melted wax or by applying caulk or sealant.

2. Install it on a dry day.

3. Seal it on the outdoor end only, allowing aspiration, if any, of dry air from the shack (assuming the shack is not in a humid greenhouse!). *Use compound, not plain electrician's tape or boots.* "Connector Seal" (p/n **791**) or similar non-drying compounds work very well. Run the seal on above the connectors and over the antenna connector until you are sure that no moisture path remains, however small.

COMPOUND

We have dissected and examined dozens of "water in the coax" examples in the last 20 years and have yet to find a single case wherein the coaxial cable was at fault. Sorry, folks, but the primary cause of failure is installer or user error! Lightning and other nature problems run a distant second. Cuts, punctures or pinholes due to manufacturer, distributor, or user handling, are rare.

Think about the construction of coaxial cable. There is air in almost all of it among the strands of the shield(s), among the strands of the stranded center conductor types, and, of course, in the tube of ASP dielectrics. Therefore, since the laws of physics apply to even small amounts of air, the aspiration possibility is inherent in almost all coax, and obviously more so in an ASP type. The point is that terminations should be properly sealed for all coaxes. It is very possible that a significant number of operators who have experienced water problems with 9913 have also had the same trouble with other coax that took longer to show up, subtly affecting performance for many months or years before full failure.

So much for **ASP** coax in the **Poor Man's Hard Line** category. The field has expanded tremendously in recent years, to include **Times Microwave System's LMR®**[8] series, new **Wireman** items, and most recently, **Belden's "Wireless"** line. These products all feature hi-tech foam dielectric with loss characteristics similar to the **ASP** types. Never before have there been so many choices in the **PMH** class, offering outstanding performance within spittin' distance of real hard line and at as little as half the cost!

---

[8] Times Microwave Systems trademark

The Leaky Hose!

The other day, while setting up a "soaker hose" for the first watering of spring, thoughts of coaxial cable came to mind. It's kind of a disease with me, you see, since having been "married" to coax for over 31 years, darn near everything reminds me of coax!

A soaker hose is designed to leak, as is a lot of coax, either for a distinct performance purpose or, unfortunately, sometimes for profit alone! Leaky coax is an antenna in itself in cases where conventional antennas will not work. You've probably noticed how your broadcast band radio goes dead in a tunnel as you drive along. No big deal, just a few commercials missed. More serious, however, would be the difficulty of transmission and reception of emergency messages, control signals, and routine information in vehicle tunnels, subways, mines, basement corridors in hospitals and government buildings, to name only a few.

Mile after mile of "leaky" coax solves this problem, and HT's, mobiles, and radio controlled devices work perfectly, thanks to coax that, at the design frequency, is "full of holes." It is run along the ceiling of all manner of tunnels and corridors either open or sealed in RFI transparent insulation, plaster, or wood. It performs just like our wire, beam, and vertical antennas as an RF radiator.

Unfortunately, some of the coax used in amateur radio is every bit as leaky for radio frequency signals as "soaker" hose is for water. Instead of green grass and beautiful blooms, however, unwelcome interference in consumer electronics and soured neighbor relations may be the result.

Proper choice of quality coaxial cable can make a major difference in station performance and good will in the QTH. The shield of the station coaxial cable should be of <u>at least</u>

90% coverage for our HF bands, and greater as the wavelength is shorter. The "holes" should become smaller at VHF and non-existent at UHF and beyond.

Checked your hose lately? Only the flowers love the "soaker!"

Simple way to check Coax Loss

We often wonder what went wrong in a coaxial cable feed line after a storm, overhaul, or switching to a new antenna. The need also arises when one doubts the claims made for a given roll of cable you've hauled home from a hamfest.

We can look up the design loss at any frequency in a table in a catalog or textbook, or break out an expensive analyzer, or even measure matched loss with a wattmeter and dummy load placed first at the station and then at the end of the coax to be checked. But, a simple test with only your transmitter and a decent bridge in or separate from the transmitter will tell you the loss in the line in decibels to a fair level of accuracy, dependent only on the quality of the bridge/wattmeter.

The most difficult job is that of disconnecting the far end of the coax under test. It can then be dead-shorted with a or left open for the test. It should make no difference. Try it both ways and learn! Apply the least power possible at 3.5 to 4MHz (to set the bridge to read full scale), thus calibrating the bridge. Switch the meter to read reflected power or SWR direct. Then, calculate the SWR or take the direct SWR reading and record it. See more detail in the "**Tip**," (next page)

If you are on the ball and you have recorded the exact length of your coax and the loss into a dummy load when it was brand new, you can compare the loss data with the test data to either pinpoint a coax problem or dismiss it. They should be at least "ballpark" close.

*Tip: Referring to the comments above, do the loss test with any new coax installation by recording power into a dummy load through a short lead at the transmitter into a dummy load, and then again into the dummy load at the end of the new run, at the same power and frequency. This data (tape it to the back of the rig) could save lots of time and money years later when troubleshooting the system by comparing original and current data and the process of elimination. Replacing a piece of coax is a lot cheaper than sending the transceiver back to the dealer for an overhaul or easier than lowering the whole antenna!

So, what coaxial cable should I buy?

We often get calls for low-loss coax and, after determining the frequency of interest; we ask how little loss is acceptable. The answer, "None!" pops up in a flash until we begin to talk money. That's when realism and compromise takes over!

There is no single, or simple, answer, since power, distance, frequency, environment, mechanical considerations and money all apply in making a choice. We consider it our job to help or at least recommend, so be prepared. If you sound the least bit uncertain when you call, we'll get nosy and then suggest the item that is best suited to your specific need.

At HF it's easy, since nearly anything will keep the loss under 2 dB for 100 feet. Translating this to power loss in a matched system with 100 watt output, anything from RG174 to RG8 size coax would work well. Note that we said "Matched System," not low SWR.."

It does make a great argument for learning more about **Balanced Line, Chapter 6**, however, with which you can run a thousand feet and stay under 2 dB loss! It would require BIG hard line for BIG bucks to beat it! and we now point you toward **Chapter 8** and "**Random size Antennas. The money you save will pay for the coax you will need to do the job with VHF, UHF and beyond!

Coaxial Cable Tables

The next four pages supply the most requested information regarding the various cables used in amateur radio. Call us for additional detail if required.

There are now many more coaxial cables than the familiar RG listings, and more are born every day. The Wireman works closely with manufacturers and is always involved in the development of new cables. Happily, we can try anything, as we are not encumbered by rules and regulations in the amateur market.

This privilege, if not abused, can ultimately provide products for the amateur community that lead the way to unique and superior cables and accessories for the world market, born of ideas from our hobby.

In the table, there are a number of coaxial cables that were created by this process and are **"Certified Quality Originals."** Most of them have been copied and now appear by several names in the trade, but they all started here in the last 31 years. They are the **bold type** items in the tables.

The information provided in the tables comes from a number of sources, some of which are in conflict with each other. This is due to standards that vary by manufacturer, federal specifications, interpretation and definition. Every value therein is provided as a means of comparison from one cable to another, for helping with choices.

Cable type & appearance	P/N WM	Mfr or Brand	Imp. ohms	VF	Cent cond	Dielec-tric	Cap. (pf/ft)	Shield	Jack-et	OD	Volts RMS	Lbs/ K ft	P/N WM	Loss, db/100 ft at freq (MHz)					Avg power - watts @ MHz					
														30	50	150	450	1GHz	30	50	150	450	900	1500
RG8	101	CQ 4XL	50.0	0.84	.108" bc	sspe	24.0	AL/tc	PVC IIA	0.405"	600	97	101	.65	.8	1.5	2.7	4.0	3300	2600	1500	830	580	440
RG8	101A	ADC	50.0	0.84	.108" bc	sspe	24.0	AL/tc	PVC	0.405"	600	97	101A	.65	.8	1.5	2.7	4.0	3300	2600	1500	830	580	440
RG8	102	CQ Flexi 4XL	50.0	0.84	19/23 bc	sspe	24.0	AL/tc	PVC IIA	0.405"	600	98	102	.65	.8	1.5	2.7	4.0	3300	2600	1500	830	580	440
RG8	103A	DRF "Bury-flex"(tm)	50.0	0.82	19/23 bc	mcfpe	24.6	AL/tc	IIIA	0.405"	600	98	103A	0.8	1.1	1.8	3.0	4.8	3300	2600	1500	830	580	440
RG8	106	CQ "Super-8"	50.0	0.82	19/23 bc	mcfpe	24.6	AL/tc	IIA	0.405"	600	98	106	0.8	1.1	1.8	3.0	4.8	3300	2600	1500	830	580	440
RG8	1000	TMW/LMR 400	50.0	0.85	.109" ccAL	ccfpe	23.9	AL/tc	IIIA	0.405"	835	90	1000	0.7	0.9	1.5	2.7	4.1	3300	2600	1500	830	580	440
RG8	9913F7	Belden	50.0	0.83	7X19 bc	hdfpe	24.6	AL/tc	TPE	0.405"	600	104	9913F7	.65	.8	1.5	2.7	4.0	4400	3400	1900	1090	750	570
LMR(R)	1005	TMW/LMR 500	50.0	0.86	.142" ccAL	ccfpe	23.6	AL/tc	IIIA	0.500"	1000	100	1005	0.5	0.7	1.2	2.2	4.0	4400	3400	1900	1090	750	570
LMR(R)	1008	TMW/LMR 600	50.0	0.87	.176" ccAL	ccfpe	23.4	AL/tc	IIIA	0.590"	1350	130	1008	0.4	0.6	1.0	1.7	3.3	5500	4200	2400	1350	930	700
LMR(R)	1009	TMW/LMR 600UF	50.0	0.85	.177" str bc	ccfpe	23.4	AL/tc	IIIA	0.590"	1350	130	1009	0.5	0.6	1.2	2.0	3.0	5500	4200	2400	1350	930	700
LMR(R)	900	TMW/LMR 900	50.0	0.87	.262" bc tube	ccpe	23.4	AL/tc	PE IIIA	0.680"	1670	290	900	0.3	0.4	0.7	1.2	1.8	8900	6900	3900	2200	1500	1100
LMR(R)	1200	TMW/LMR 1200	50.0	0.88	.349" bc tube	ccpe	23.1	AL/tc	PE IIIA	0.920"	2000	510	1200	0.2	0.3	0.5	0.9	1.4	6900	9700	5500	3100	2100	1600
LMR(R)	1700	TMW/LMR 1700	50.0	0.89	.527" bc tube	ccpe	22.8	AL/tc	PE IIIA	1.350"	3000	740	1700	0.2	0.2	0.4	0.6	1.0	3900	15600	8700	4800	3200	2400

Cable type & appearance	P/N	Mfr or Brand	Imp. (ohm)	VF	Cond	Dielec-	Cap. (pf/ft)	Shield	Jack-et	OD	Watts RMS	Lb/k.ft	P/N	Loss, dB/100 ft at freq (MHz)					Avg power - watts @ MHz					
														30	50	150	450	1GHz	30	50	150	450	900	1500
8X	115	CQ Mini-8 Black	50.0	0.78	19/29 bc	mc/fpe	28.0	bc	PVC Chr.	0.242"	500	41	115	1.5	2.1	3.8	6.7	11.2	1200	1100	800	370	280	200
8X	116	CQ Mini-8 IIA	50.0	0.78	19/29 bc	mc/fpe	28.0	bc	PVC IIA	0.242"	500	41	116	1.5	2.1	3.8	6.7	11.2	1200	1100	800	370	280	200
8X	117	CQ Mini-8 Marine/Mobile	50.0	0.72	19/29 bc	dfpp	29.1	tc	PE IIIA	0.242"	1500	45	117	2	2.4	4.1	7.5	12.0	1300	1200	700	450	320	250
Dialcoax	166	Shielded balanced line	150Ω	0.82	18ccs	pe	16.2	al/atl	PVC	2.272	1400	75	166	1.4	n/a	n/a	n/a	n/a	n/a	n/a	n/a	n/a	n/a	n/a
8X	118	CQ Mini-8 Lo-Loss Flex	50.0	0.81	19/29 bc	mc/fpe	24.6	AL/tc	TPE	0.242"	300	42	118YY	1.4	1.8	3.3	6.0	7.6	1300	1200	700	450	320	280
RG11/U	121	Mil Spec type	75Ω	0.66	7/0.0159 bc	pe	20.6	bc	PVC IIA	0.405"	300	32	121	0.83	1.3	2.5	4.5	7.2	1900	1500	620	250	170	50
RG8U	124	CQ "Bazooka"	50.0	0.66	.082" bccs	pe	29.8	tc	PE IIIA	0.195"	1400	29	124	1.8	2.9	5.1	9.7	16.5	880	450	170	85	80	10
RG58U	125	Mil Spec	53.5	0.66	.032 bc	pe	28.8	tc	PVC	0.195"	100	28	125	1.6	2.9	5.1	9.7	16.5	550	450	170	85	50	10
RG58/U	126	Mil Spec	52Ω	0.66	19/0.0071" bc	pe	29.6	tc	PVC	0.195"	100	29	126	2.05	3.7	6.8	13.6	22.8	550	450	170	85	50	10
RG58C	127	Mil Spec	50Ω	0.66	19/0.0071" bc	pe	30.8	tc	PVC IIA	0.195"	100	29	127	2.05	3.7	6.8	13.6	22.8	550	450	170	85	50	10
58	129YY	CQ 58 Lo-Loss Flex	52.0	0.78	19/.0071" bc	mc/fpe	24.6	AL/tc	TPE	0.195"	340	29	129YY	1.3	2.9	4.9	9.1	15.3	880	680	360	220	140	120

Cable type & appearance	P/N W/M	Mfr or Brand	Imp. ohm	VF	Cent cond	Dielec-tric	Cap. (pf/ft)	Shield	Jack-et	OD	Volts RMS	Lb/M k ft	P/N W/M	Loss, db/100 ft at freq (MHz)					Avg power r- watts @ MHz					
														30	50	150	450	1GHz	30	50	150	450	900	1500
RG58A/U	135	MilSpec	75Ω	0.66	.027 bccs	pe	26.5	bc	PVC IIA	0.242	1700	34	135	2	2.4	4.1	7.5	12.0	1090	870	270	140	80	40
RG62A/U	141	MilSpec	93Ω	0.84	.0257 bccs	sspe	13.5	bc	PVC IIA	0.242	750	38	141	1.7	1.9	3.3	5.6	8.7	1090	870	270	140	80	40
RG83/U	165	MilSpec	35Ω	0.66	.102 bc	pe	44.0	bc	PVC IIA	0.405	3700	122	165	4.8	5.6	10.7	18.6	29.0	5300	3300	1240	460	290	100
RG142B/U	153	MilSpec	50Ω	0.695	.037 sccs	pte	29.2	sc&c	IX	0.195	1400	43	153	2.3	2.7	4.8	8.7	13.5	7600	6700	2200	1050	730	500
LMR 100A	138	TMW	50Ω	0.66	0.018 bccs	pe	30.8	Albc	PVC	0.110	2000	15	138	3.9	5.1	8.9	15.8	24.1	230	180	100	60	50	40
RG174A/U	139	MilSpec	50Ω	0.66	7/0.0057 ccs	pe	30.8	tc	IIA	0.100	1100	8	139	5.1	5.8	10.5	21.4	34.0	180	150	47	25	18	7
RG178/U	140	MilSpec	50Ω	0.66	7/0.0057 ccs	pe	30.8	tc	PVC	0.100	1100	8	140	5.1	5.8	10.5	21.4	34.0	180	150	47	25	18	7
RG178B/U	157	MilSpec	50Ω	0.695	7 / .004 sccs	pte	29.0	sc	IX	0.072	750	6	157	6.7	8.7	15.1	26.3	39.6	620	530	230	120	75	40
RG188/U	159	MilSpec	50Ω	0.695	7/0.0057 sccs	pte	29.0	sc	IX	0.105	900	17	159	4.9	5.6	10.1	18.6	29.0	1070	890	390	211	140	60
RG213/U(E)	**110**	**Enhanced Mil Spec**	**50.0**	**0.66**	**7/0.0295 bc**	**pe**	**30.8**	**bc**	**IIA**	**0.405**	**3700**	**100**	**110**	**1.3**	**1.5**	**2.6**	**4.9**	**8.2**	**3200**	**2400**	**730**	**310**	**210**	**70**
RG213/U	113	MilSpec	50Ω	0.66	7/0.0295 bc	pe	30.8	bc	IIA	0.405	3700	100	113	1.28	1.5	2.6	4.9	8.2	3300	2400	730	310	210	70
RG213/U(C)	113C	Commercial	50Ω	0.66	7/0.0295 bc	pe	30.8	bc	PVC	0.405	3700	100	113C	1.28	1.5	2.6	4.9	8.2	3300	2400	730	310	210	70
RG213/U(P)	**113PE**	**CQ Rugged Buriable**	**50.0**	**0.66**	**7/0.0295 bc**	**pe**	**30.8**	**bc, water block**	**PE IIIA**	**0.405**	**3700**	**100**	**113PE**	**1.3**	**1.5**	**2.6**	**4.9**	**8.2**	**3200**	**2400**	**730**	**310**	**210**	**70**

Cable type & appearance	P/N M/M	Mfr or Brand	Imp. ohm	VF	Cent cond	Dielec. trc	Cap. (pf/ft)	Shield	Jacket	OD	Volts RMS	Lb/1 Kft	P/N M/M	Loss dB/100 ft rating (MHz)					Avg power - watts @ MHz					
														30	50	150	450	1GHz	30	50	150	450	900	1500
RG214U	111	MilSpec	50.0	0.66	7/0.0296 sc	pe	30.8	sc&tc	IIA	0.425"	5000	125	111	1.05	1.3	2.3	4.7	8.0	3200	2500	830	315	200	50
RG214U(C)	112	Commercial	50.0	0.66	7/0.0296 tc	pe	30.8	tc/tc	—	0.425"	5000	125	112	1.05	1.3	2.3	4.7	8.0	3200	2500	830	315	200	50
RG217U	142	MilSpec	50.0	0.66	.105 bc	pe	30.8	bc&bc	IIA	0.545"	7000	202	142	0.71	0.9	1.7	3.2	5.2	5200	3300	1240	460	290	100
RG217U	142A	CQ Flexi-217	**50.0**	0.66	7x0.057 bc	**pe**	**30.8**	**bc&bc**	PE	**0.545"**	7000	202	**142**	**0.7**	**0.9**	**1.7**	**3.2**	**5.2**	**5200**	**3300**	**1240**	**460**	**290**	**100**
RG223U	143	MilSpec	50.0	0.66	.035 sc	pe	29.4	sc&sc	IIA	0.211"	1900	36	143	2.12	2.8	4.8	8.6	13.3	610	530	180	84	59	18
RG303U	154	MilSpec	50.0	0.695	.039 sccs	ptfe	29.4	sc	IX	0.170"	1900	30	154	2.03	2.6	4.6	8.26	12.7	760	620	220	105	71	20
RG316U	160	MilSpec	50.0	0.695	7/0.0067 sccs	ptfe	29.4	sc	IX	0.102"	1200	12	160	3.86	5.0	8.7	15.4	23.3	1060	890	390	210	150	50
RG400U	149	MilSpec	50.0	0.695	19/0.0117 bc	ptfe	29.4	sc&sc	IX	0.195"	1900	50	149	2.2	2.8	4.8	8.6	13.2	750	620	230	105	73	29
RG393U	150	MilSpec	50.0	0.695	7/0.0312 sc	ptfe	29.4	sc&sc	IX	0.390"	4000	165	150	0.72	0.9	1.7	3.2	5.1	2000	1500	720	1050	730	290
RG63U	163	MilSpec	125.0	0.84	.025	sspe	9.7	bc	IIA	0.405"	1000	88	163	0.72	1.1	1.9	5.0	6.5	N/A	N/A	N/A	N/A	N/A	N/A

Legend: bc=bare copper; tc=tinned copper; sc=silvered copper; ccs =copper-clad steel; ccAL=copper-clad Aluminum sspe= semi-solid polyethylene; mcf=microcell foam; ccf=closed cell foam; hdf=high density foam; dfpp=dense foam polypropylene; ptfe=teflon type; PVC=polyvinylchloride; IIA=Class 2 PVC (non-contaminating); IIIA=polyethylene (pe) ; Class 3: TPE,TPR=thermoplastic rubber IX=Class 9 teflon® type (ptfe)

The next page is our popular old faithful loss chart, which is useful for comparing coax loss all at one time and in one place. There are a few part numbers that reference items now known by other numbers or names explained in the text, but the useful data are intact.

The balance of this page is open for your notes as new goals are met in manufacturing, and new cables are created.

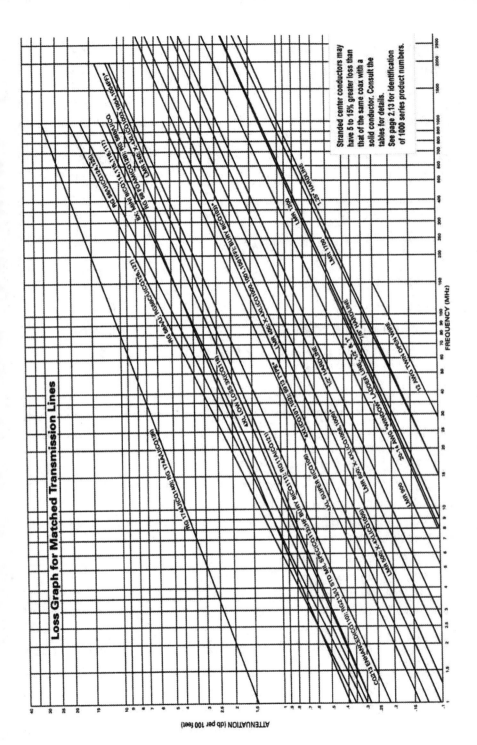

Loss Graph for Matched Transmission Lines

Stranded center conductors may have 5 to 15% greater loss than that of the same coax with a solid conductor. Consult the tables for details.
See page 2.13 for identification of 1000 series product numbers.

ATTENUATION (db per 100 feet)

FREQUENCY (MHz)

What's in a Name?

Did you ever wonder where the strange names for connectors came from?

For example, the **UHF** term for the class we all know as the PL259/SO239 type — stands for **U**ltra **H**igh **F**requency, right? Well maybe so, perhaps **HF** seemed Ultra High back in the 1930's when E. Clark Quackenbush invented this connector.

Then there's the **N** type — for microwave, invented and named after Paul Neill of Bell Labs.

The **C** also has a logical background. It was the first "quick disconnect" type, cooked up by Carl Concelman, of Amphenol.

The guys then apparently got together with the little **BNC**, which stands for **B**ayonet **N**eill **C**oncelman, and, you guessed it, the **TNC**, for **T**hreaded **N**eill **C**oncelman.

I just finished installing an **SMA** (**S**ure **M**ighty **A**ggravating)!

The Good Old PL259

The PL-259 is the most commonly used connector in amateur radio. There are all kinds, insulated with a variety of dielectrics and plated with nickel, silver and gold, and the quality varies from excellent to terrible. There are just as many ways to install them, and every year we see new pet methods in the periodicals, journals and handbooks.

We are told that they are not a constant impedance device and therefore their insertion loss becomes significant as the chosen frequency of use becomes higher, and that when we reach VHF and UHF, they are terrible and "N" types are the only way to go.

One wonders why they are called "UHF type" in text and catalog? Was there a time that they were the only type available and everything was hooked up to binding posts?

Don't put down the PL!

At the risk of shattering some illusions, the following paragraphs are offered in the interest of saving you from some grief and for cutting your connector costs.

First of all, the good old "PL" is an excellent connector, and it will satisfy the great majority of all amateur connector needs. The insertion loss of a properly installed PL259 at frequencies up through VHF and beyond is probably the smallest problem your system will ever see. If you were to switch out every PL259 and SO239 in your station for male and female "N" connectors at 3 to 6 times the cost and have them all professionally installed, your signal reports and "S" meter readings would be about the same as usual. The odds of your speaker blaring, "Wow, did you get a new amplifier for Christmas?" as a result of the effort are about the same as those of hearing "You've just won the Lottery or Reader's Digest Sweepstakes!"

Alan Bloom, N1AL, used an HP8753 RF network analyzer and a test setup to compare the losses of the lowly UHF connector to the highly respected N connector. The results are shown below[1]:

Frequency Mhz	N Type Loss (db)	UHF Type Loss (db)
1.8	0	0
30	0	0
100	0	0
150	0	0.01
200	0	0.015
450	0	0.09
600	0	0.13
900	0	0.33
1000	0.025	0.4
1300	0.05	0.43
1600	0.025	0.25
2000	0.025	0.01

A similar comparison can be made between nickel and silver plated PL259's, but now we can begin to make choices for some very valid reasons.

There is no doubt that silver is a better electrical conductor than the various nickel alloys used in the plating of RF connectors. The point is whether there is a significant difference, and if so, is it worth the higher price? The answer is like comparing an $8000 car to a $30,000 model – either will get you to work and home again. One will make you feel better, impress those around you, and go faster than the other, but both will shed the rain, fall apart without maintenance, die without fuel, and earn a citation when driven through a red light.

A well-made PL259 with silver, nickel, or gold plating and properly installed, will, at amateur frequencies up through VHF, serve equally well within the ability of any of us to discern a difference.

Silver over-rated

Under laboratory conditions, with appropriate instrumentation, one might see a difference at VHF or UHF of the surface conductivity, but, surprisingly, it would probably be in

---

[1]From QST, January 1998, by permission, and with thanks to N1AL.

favor of the good quality nickel plate! Research, reported in the proceedings of the IREE in Australia way back in 1970 by A. M. Fowler and since then throughout the industry, shows clearly that, "The RF conductivity of an electroplated metal is normally lower than that of the pure, cast and wrought, metal." Thus silver-plating a connector often increases the RF loss of a copper alloy conductor rather than reducing it as expected.

The actual plating procedure is most critical both in makeup and in technique, and studies show that low-priced connectors do not follow such discipline; in fact, many electronic engineers have a tendency to ignore the phenomenon!

Saving grace!

There is, however, one big plus for silver plated connectors, even if it is not better RF propagation: It solders beautifully and very easily, and for the guy who installs 2 or 3 PL's a year and is less than skilled at soldering, it is easily worth the extra few pennies!

How about Teflon® versus phenolic dielectric? Consider what the dielectric does in a connector: With its high dielectric strength it insulates the center conductor from the connector body and keeps the center equi-distant from the surrounding wall. Good PL's are available with Teflon®, phenolic, and other dielectrics, and most will do the job equally well within the bounds of our requirements. One exception would be if arcing were a possibility such as in the connectors to and from a high reactance load like a tuner or amplifier. Teflon® is best since arcing doesn't leave a carbon trail that will allow arcing more readily with each subsequent high voltage incident.

The best choices then, considering performance, cost, ease of installation, are:

> Silvered center conductor
> Teflon® or phenolic dielectric
> Silvered body for the occasional installer, or
> Nickel-plated body for the more skilled solderer
> Nickel or silver plated shell

Impressed by Gold plated connectors? Forget it! About 25% lower conductivity than Silver! Sucker bait!

Quality Counts

There is one final consideration – quality. There is a lot of junk out there, so be careful. If the price is too good to be true, it probably is. The "cheapies" often feel rough and the shell grates or drags when screwed on. The "Teflon" is actually some other white-colored plastic that softens when soldered. The body is poorly "staked" or rolled into the dielectric, allowing separation under stress. The plating can be so thin that the corrosion resistance is poor.

Things to look for: Look for consistency and a good "feel." In a big box full are they all the same? Are there filings or metal scraps in the bottom of the box? Wiggle the center pin. It should be tight and not rotatable. The inside diameter of the pin should accommodate a 10 AWG solid wire with ease, or a #35 drill bit. Look at the dielectric. It should be brownish phenolic or snow-white Teflon®[2], not clear or grayish white. As for price, a silver-"teflon" PL for $1.00 or less is probably no bargain. The cheapest good nickel-phenolic is usually at least $0.90 to $1.10, good silver-Teflon® PL's range from $1.25 to $3.00 or more.

PL 259 Installation

Ever since the origin of the PL259, pet methods for its installation have appeared from everywhere, including out of the woodwork. One wonders if anyone has ever read the directions and realized that the basic method that was born

---

[2] Teflon is a trademark of Dupont.

with the connector is still the best and easiest way to get the job done correctly.

This installation guide is based on the original and is followed by most professional installers. Hints and commentary along the way are added to share with you things that we have found that make the procedure go well consistently.

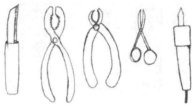

Please take a few minutes and read the whole section before beginning the procedure, and then practice on a scrap or two.

The right tools help a lot — our favorites include:

- ✓ A simple ohmmeter – a must!
- ✓ Sharp, sturdy, short blade or electrician's knife.
- ✓ Pair of plain slack jawed pliers.
- ✓ Curved blade coax cutter (side cutters work if that's all you have, but rotate and make several shallow cuts to avoid distorting the soft copper – see later notes on stranded).
- ✓ 100 to 200 watt soldering iron with fairly heavy tip (for good heat retention) but pyramid-shape pointed tip that will easily work in the soldering area around the holes of a PL259. The taper of the point should allow it to go into the hole but not through it. Molten solder heats the braid, not direct contact with the iron.[3]
- ✓ Damp sponge or rag wad for cooling and iron tip wiping.
- ✓ Pair of sharp, pointed side cutters.
- ✓ Pair of cuticle scissors (yes, cuticle scissors!)
- ✓ Small headed, very fine brass or steel bristle brush (optional, but handy. A necessity with "N" connectors and PL259 and 2 piece "N" reducers for combing braid.
- ✓ Dry rag.

---

[3] The small torches made by "Solder-It" do nicely as well, but require practice and good technique.

- ✓ Tube of silicone grease (or Vaseline in a pinch).
- ✓ And, of course, a good grade of rosin core solder (50-60% tin, 40-50% lead) (Still preferred over the lead-free type with higher melt temperature).
- ✓ Also handy is a bottle of alcohol (the rubbing variety – 91% isopropyl is best, but 70% is OK in a pinch. Potable types are best reserved for other pursuits!), and a few Q-tips.

FOR .405" COAX (RG213, RG8 type ETC. WITH 12 GAUGE OR SMALLER CENTER CONDUCTORS)

1. Place the COUPLING RING or SHELL on the coax, threads toward the work area.

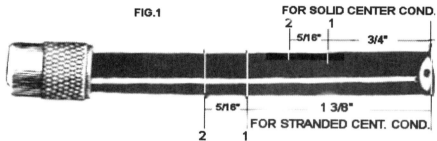

FIG.1

FOR SOLID CENTER COND.

2   1

5/16"   3/4"

5/16"   1 3/8"

FOR STRANDED CENT. COND.

2   1

2. Start with a clean cutoff end on the coax and measure back to points 1 and 2, making a visible cut as a marker at each point (fig.1). Note the different dimensions for solid and stranded center conductor. It is well worth your time to review the tinning procedure described under "Large Center Conductors" several pages ahead, due to the many different types of stranding and the differences in connectors.

3. At the appropriate point (1), cut through the jacket, braid, and dielectric all the way to the center conductor, then all the way around it, without nicking it.

TIP: Bend the coax just slightly to open to check the depth of the cut. Continue to carefully cut and slightly bend until the conductor is totally visible. It helps to practice on a piece of scrap a few times if you are new at this game. Remove all of the loosened jacket and braid. They should slide off easily. Do not attempt to pull or twist off the dielectric unless you can do so easily <u>without</u> exposing additional braid and/or dielectric.

4. Pry the dielectric off by opposing two pairs of side cutters carefully so as not to nick the center conductor (fig. 3). Dielectric difficult to remove can be cut several times so that smaller chunks can be slid or pried off (fig. 4). If all else fails, cut and lightly separate numerous smaller chunks and split them with the side cutters.

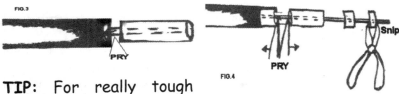

TIP: For really tough dielectric removal, follow the multiple cut procedure above, then tin the center conductor and immediately slip off the smaller chunks with ease while the copper conductor is still hot. With practice, tinning stranded types with solid polyethylene dielectric right after step (3) makes the removal a cinch, if done quickly.

5. Refer back to (fig. 1), point (2), and cut through the jacket without cutting the braid. Discard the jacket scrap.

6. With the cuticle shears (or very sharp side cutters) trim the braid at the shoulder at about 45 degrees (fig. 5) to approximate the dimension [c] in (fig. 6). The objective here is simply to be sure  that no scrap of braid, foil or whatever will get past the shoulder and cause a short or even a small gap between the two conductors, making arcing possible.

Large Center Conductors

Before we move on, note that special attention is necessary for preparing the larger center conductors of the new generation of low-loss RG8-size coaxes. Most of these, whether solid or stranded, are about 0.108 inch in diameter, and the inside diameter of the PL259 pins differs by manufacturer from as much as nearly 0.120 inch down to less than 0.100 inch[4].

The solid conductors, properly prepared, are not a problem, but the various stranded models can easily generate useless fury, especially since it is so easy to do it wrong!

Here are a few facts on the subject that might help you establish the right state of mind:

- ✓ Given good quality connectors and coaxial cable designed for the job, the two **WILL** mate if properly prepared.
- ✓ It is **NEVER** necessary or proper to remove one or more strands to make it happen.
- ✓ No matter how certain you are that your particular event is the exception to items (1.) and (2.), the odds that you are correct approach a million to one against you!

Having said this, here is a method that works every time, and we hope it works as well for you as it has for us over the years. Remember the two choices in (fig. 1)? It relates to the sum of dimension **b** and **B** in (fig. 6), whereby one prepares at least 5/8 inch more center conductor than is needed for the job. Here again a little tinning on the cut end before removing **ANY** dielectric is a big help in the rest of the preparation.

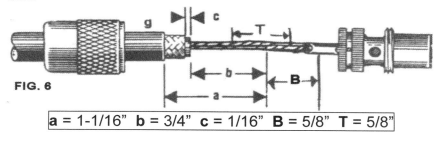

FIG. 6

| a = 1-1/16" | b = 3/4" | c = 1/16" | B = 5/8" | T = 5/8" |

---

[4]Take a minute to read *"The Good Old PL259"* before you buy them again.

Tinning is a very important step for the large, multi-strand center conductors since they are tightly packed and will, without tinning, "unpack" when cut to where they won't fit into the center pin. If a single one of the strands doesn't make it, you'll have a dead short and a headache. See the diagram (fig. 6) and note the tinning area (T), which will make a safe cut area when tinned. The backward plug is used to keep the earlier lightly tinned strands together while the (T) portion is being tinned.

7. The cut to satisfy dimension (b) can then be made by carefully applying pressure to the cutter's handles at several points of rotation to avoid any chance of distortion. Another backward plug test will show if a high spot requires scraping and cleaning before applying the connector body to the coax. Coax examples so involved are **CQ102, CQ106, 103A, Belden 9913F7, Times LMR and Andrew Cinta**, and the like.

8. For stranded center conductors of normal RG8 types, touch the hot iron to the tip and tin or flow just enough solder among the strands to ensure that all of them are "welded" together. It should now slip easily into the connector's hollow center pin. Prove this by slipping the center pin backwards over the center pin as a test (see fig.6). Optionally, try tinning the stranded center conductor before you do anything else, as in fig. 1, showing a 7 strand and a 19 strand coax end, with solid PE and foam PE, before and after (fig1a). The strands are

fig 1

fig 1a

locked together tightly and the stripping was easy while the copper was still hot, guaranteeing a perfect fit in the connector pin.

9. At this point, some directions call for tinning the braid before installing the connector body. This is difficult to do without melting the dielectric and mis-shaping the exposed braid and is not necessary for a perfect installation. We do not recommend it.

10. Clean the connector body with a Q-tip and alcohol inside and out. Some technicians run a fine ¼ inch file over the holes to improve the "solder take" on nickel-plated connectors, and others use a pencil eraser to buff the hole area. This helps assure successful soldering, if needed – especially on connectors that have been kicking around in the "junk box" for a while. Do it before the alcohol cleaning, and be sure all metal filings and dirt are gone before proceeding. We do not find this necessary on the many brand new connectors installed in the shop. The silver-plated models "take" solder beautifully and are always the best if you just do one or two connectors a year.

11. One last point here. Please **DO NOT** fall for the oft-repeated suggestion to drill the solder holes larger as an installation aid. This doubles the risk of melting the dielectric with too much solder, allows the iron to penetrate the braid, and shortens the distance for potential arcing, if not direct shorting. Millions of these connectors have been made by dozens of manufacturers since their origin in the '30's, and the hole size hasn't changed – a pretty good sign that the size is correct as it is.

12. Place a tad of silicone grease at point (g) and start threading the plug body onto the PVC or Polyethylene by hand for as far as you can, and, if necessary, grip the cable tightly by hand near the plug and screw it on the rest of the way with the pliers, carefully ratcheting (without stripping) on the notched plug body. You should feel the dielectric "hit home" against the back of the pin and see braid through the four solder holes (figs. 7, 9). Test with

FIG.7 FIG. 9

13. The connector body and the braid showing need to come to solder-flow temperature at the same moment. Summon a helper, if possible, to hold the coil of coax and hold the plug on the bench with each hole up in turn. Using a hot iron, touch into the first hole (fig. 8) and apply solder.

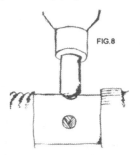

FIG.8

Work it a bit for 4 to 8 seconds only, not trying to finish, and move to the next hole. The plug should now be pre-heated from your effort at hole 1 so that holes 2, 3, and 4 should flow and fill nicely in 4 - 8 seconds each, and number 1 can be touched up and finished in a few seconds more. If the whole process takes longer than 40 seconds, there is danger that the plug is overheated. The vinyl jacket could melt and separate, or solder could flow past the braid and short circuit the plug. Cool it by grasping it with the damp rag, set it aside for 5-10 minutes; test it, then clean the area carefully and go at it again.

HINT: The old trick of folding the braid back over the jacket and then screwing on the plug is just plain stupid. It might have been OK for temporary use at 5 watts, but never for finished work at higher power at any frequency. The threads in the plug cut the braid wires into tiny pieces and metallic dust, and with any amount of continuing flexing, a short, an open, or an intermittent becomes a certainty.

14. Finally, flow solder into the tip on a touch-and-go basis until it flows about halfway in and until the outer tip is sealed full. Excess solder on the center pin should be wiped off with a rag scrap while molten. Scraping the pin

---

[5] **You cannot test too often. Do it at every step to save time and trouble later.**

after cooling removes the silver plating and raises the resistance in the connection.

15. Let it cool. Screwing the coupling shell into place promptly helps with the cooling.

16. **TEST** it – again!

Good Work!

For .195", .242", OD Cable (RG58, 59, 8X, 142, 303, etc)

1. Cleanly cut the cable end and slide the coupling ring and the appropriate adaptor (UG175 or 176) onto the coax. Remove ¾" of jacket. Carefully avoid nicking the braid.

2. Fan the braid slightly back as shown, then slide the adaptor inside the braid to the end of the jacket.

3. Shape the braid to the adaptor, brushing it straight and uniformly. Trim short of the threads if necessary with the cuticle scissors. *If this is a lo-loss coax with a foil shield under the braid, snip and peel away the foil from the exposed center conductor dielectric.*

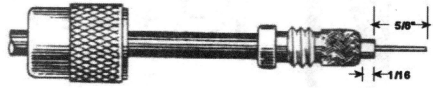

4. Bare the center conductor, without nicking, to 5/8" and tin if stranded, after finger-twisting it to keep all of the strands together.

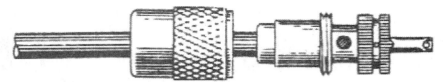

5. Carefully press the screw plug assembly onto the adaptor and screw the adaptor into it while maintaining closing pressure on both parts. The idea is to keep the braid undisturbed as much as possible so that a goodly number of strands appear in each hole while keeping the adaptor even with the end of the jacket.

6. **TEST AGAIN!**

7. Solder center conductor into the pin only enough to secure it. This holds the assembly in place while the 4 holes are soldered.

8. Solder the four holes as directed for the bigger cable, uniting braid, adaptor and plug assembly. The solder should flow into the hole and braid until the hole is sealed. Remember – high heat, short time!

9. **TEST AGAIN!**

Finally, flow solder into the tip on a touch-and-go basis until it goes about halfway in and until the outer tip is sealed full. The touch-and-go procedure is more critical with the smaller center conductor. You don't want to fill the pin all the way back to the coax dielectric. Touch and go until the outer end, no more than half of its length, is full. Excess solder on the center pin should be wiped off with a rag scrap while molten. Scraping the pin removes the silver plating and makes an imperfect connection.

Screw shell onto plug. Cool, and then, **TEST AGAIN!**

Another winner! Whew!

<u>New Two Piece "N" Installation</u>

This connector has all but replaced the clamp type Mil Spec UG21B/U[6] with its 6 or more parts and twice the price. It is also more practical, since both shield and pin are soldered, a feature that wipes out the problem of the cold weather contraction of the heavy copper conductor in what we refer to as the "9913" type of coax.[7] The risk of the connector being pulled off the coax by its own weight is also minimized by the soldered shield and the strong grip on the jacket by the threaded body, similar to the PL259.

All in all, there is little or no reason not to deploy this connector in any amateur installation where an "N" is the best choice for the job. We urge you, as always, to gather all of the information you can for the choice of connectors, and consider the possibility that an "N" model in your project might not be needed unless UHF or higher is involved.

Check out "**The Good Old PL**" at the beginning of this chapter for a performance comparison.

---

[6] Email us for the old style "N" instructions, if required.
[7] See Chapter 2

Speaking of the PL259, it is worth your time to go over the procedures for installing one before starting on the "N," since the fundamentals and technique are similar for both and will not be repeated here.

Let's get to work:

1. Our example for preparation is a piece of the lo-loss RG8 class of coax with a 0.108" OD center conductor, and if you learn how to do it right, you'll have no trouble with any coax from 0.100" to 0.545" OD (RG174/U to RG217/U). This means that you need to flip over to the PL259 installation pages right now. The steps described there are all you need to follow, using the dimensions given in (fig.1) below, for the matter at hand.

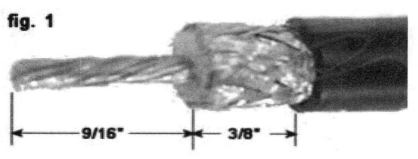

fig. 1

|← 9/16" →|← 3/8" →|

2. Having prepared and tested the coax for the connector, look at (fig. 2) next, a cross sectional sketch of the body.

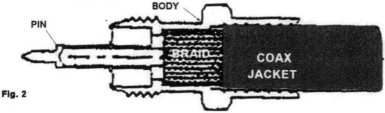

Fig. 2

3. Apply a tad of silicone grease to the outside of the jacket, just at the end, to allow the body to be screwed onto the coax. You should see the center conductor through the solder hole in the pin when the jacket has entered about

an eighth of an inch into the body. If it doesn't pass the hole in the next turn or so, it has missed the opening in the pin or the conductor has not been properly sized, and you'll need to unscrew the body and re-check your work. The coax center conductor must be no larger than 0.108" in diameter.

4. **TEST** with ohmmeter.

5. Solder through and including the two holes in the body, using the same technique as for a PL259, and cool with damp rag promptly (fig. 3). Hold the soldering iron tip firmly against the pin very near the hole and touch the solder to the center of the hole until it flows. A quarter inch of small solder is usually enough to anchor the pin to the conductor and seal the hole. Cool with damp rag.

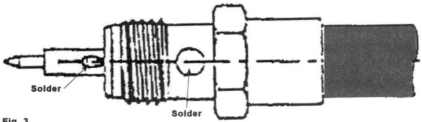

Fig. 3

TIP: The 0.031" rosin core solder is best for this. Cut off the melted tip so you can see the tiny core or rosin, then, with a pliers, squeeze the solder a half inch or so in from the end until a tiny droplet of the flux appears at the end – not enough to drip. When you touch the hot conductor this drop flows quickly and almost seems to suck the solder into the hole.

5. **TEST** BETWEEN AND AFTER THE TWO SOLDERING JOBS.

6. Screw the sleeve or shell section onto the body section and tighten securely with two flat-faced wrenches (fig. 4).

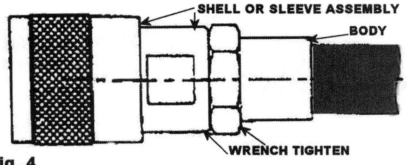

Fig. 4

7. One final test and you're set to go. If shrink tube is appropriate, a 2-inch piece from the back of the sleeve down over the coax is used. Three-quarter inch ID (before shrinking) lined or plain shrink tube is required.

FOR 0.195," 0.242," OD COAX (RG58, 59, 142, 303, ETC.)

This is handled just like the procedure for the PL259, with slightly different dimensions to allow for the closed end pin in the "N" connector. Several figures from the PL259 section are modified below to show dimensions for the 2-piece "N" assembly. The figures here are in millimeters because the usual fractions of an inch are too unwieldy and difficult to work with. See the conversion table on page 65 if required.

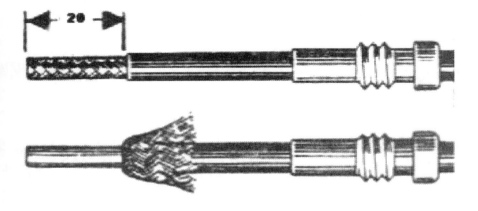

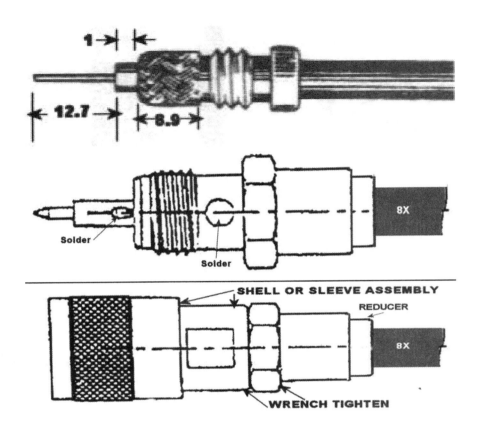

All right, 20 mm is a tad more than 25/32," 12.7 mm is ½," 1 mm is a tad more than 1/32," and 8.9 mm is a tad more than 11/32," OK?

New Ham Commandment I

Thou shall not bear false witness......Thanks to your "Elmer" a true friend for getting you on the right track and for helping you to get your first license. Now work with him and by yourself with this and other references to double check what you've learned so far to broaden your skills, upgrade, and get the full enjoyment and satisfaction from this great hobby.

Look for nine more New Ham Commandments here and there in The Wirebook!

Adapters

SEX!

Got your attention? Take your copy of **The Wirebook** to the shack, close the door, and read on -----

It's one of the biggest, most expensive problems in amateur radio, in spite of the fact that it is easily avoided. Male and female mating, gender change, physical characteristics, mismatches and emergency enabling are involved, and mistakes almost inevitably prevent the intended continuity. *(Down, boy!)*

Sorry to spoil the titillating illusion, but the subject is connectors. (But now you can look at them with a sly grin!).

Don't run off, though, unless you've never bought the wrong connector or adapter for use in your amateur radio activity! Here are a few simple definitions and hints that will help you get it right the first time.

First of all, the terminology. Take a look at the illustration below and the names of the parts shown:

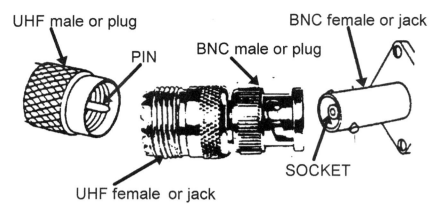

UHF male or plug

PIN

BNC male or plug

BNC female or jack

SOCKET

UHF female or jack

ADAPTER, UHF female(socket) to BNC male(pin)

Adapters are used when two or more incompatible items must be joined. Connectors are defined by series, such as the "BNC" series, the "N" series, the "UHF" series, etc.

In the connector field, a device for getting from one series to another is called an "inter-series adapter," and yes, within a series, it's an "intra-series" adapter.

Note that, with no exception you'll be likely to encounter, the "female" part is a "socket" into which a "male" part, a "pin," is inserted. This relates to the center conductor of the coax in the junction and defines the coaxial connector.

In practically all RF connectors the **"plug"** is the male connector that contains the pin, and the **"jack"** is the female which contains the socket. The terms, "plug" or "jack" are not necessarily synonymous with "pin" or "socket," and can indeed be cause for error. Connectors for other than RF are a whole other ball game, so be very careful with the above terminology, since a "plug" or "jack" can describe a housing full of either "pins" or "sockets," and gender is either "standard" or "reversed," depending on the whim of the genius or madman who designed the connection. Thinking back to the name of this story, the terms, "plugs" and "jacks" are something you should understand and be aware of, but should learn to avoid in RF work, just like the "ladies of the night," lest you get something other than what you thought you had ordered!

Adapters combine two or more connectors, each of which must be defined to avoid error. In the example depicted, calling it, "a BNC male to UHF female adapter" will get you what you see. Calling it "the thingie to go from the whoozy on my HT to the PL on my coax to the antenna" might or might not! Why take the chance? Many a "junk box" contains an assortment of expensive mistakes.

Remember: Describe the item you want – not what you want it to fit, by series (UHF, N, BNC, etc.) and gender. Use the simple terms, "male" or "pin," and "female" or "socket," and you'll be getting it right the first time!

Verify your choices by working with images and descriptions on our web site (www.thewireman.com). Use the numbers to identify your need or define it. Snap a picture if that works for you. If all else fails, ask The Wireman for help!

Crimp-on Connectors

Many amateurs are wary of this type of termination, and the uncertainty is justified if the reference is the "F" connector on most television hook-ups. These little "cheapies" are installed with inexpensive crimpers, pliers, or whatever, but seem to work OK.

This is not surprising if one considers the fact that the center conductor of the coax is the "pin" and the slightest touch of the sparse braid to the connector body is sufficient to provide a ground path for the composite audio-video, receive-only signal.

None of us, I hope, would even think of using such a connector in a 1500 watt station, and yet we see crimp-types all of the time on the jumpers we buy and the ready to use hard line and "Poor Man's Hard Line" assemblies, so it is obvious that such products can be safe to use, even at full power.

The assurance we need is found in the quality of the connectors, the proper tools, and the skill of the installer. A typical crimp and die set for the job is a precision tool which ranges in cost from $75 to over $200, and the connectors are in the same price class as the Mil Spec clamp or solder types. It is an unusual radio operator that does enough connector installation to justify such equipment.

Some of the miniature connectors such as SMA's and smaller are better suited to crimp-on types than solder types, and are usually more reliable, due to the manual difficulty and the high temperature effects of soldering tiny devices.

In general, there is no significant performance justification to insist on only solder or solder-clamp installations by a professional installer who guarantees his work, crimps included, for amateur related operations.

Possible exceptions for individual choice are unsupported or oft-strained heavy lines on crank-up towers and installations where temperature differentials, seasonal or otherwise, are possible. Strain conditions should always employ cable grips to protect any connector style.

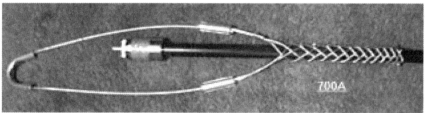

This is a sample cable grip – see more about them on page 67 before putting them to work.

Conversion Table – Inches/Millimeters

INCHES		MM	INCHES		MM
1/64	0.0156	0.397	33/64	0.5156	13.097
1/32	0.0313	0.794	17/32	0.5313	13.494
3/64	0.0466	1.191	35/64	0.5469	13.891
1/16	0.0625	1.588	9/16	0.5625	14.288
5/64	0.0781	1.984	37/64	0.5781	14.684
3/32	0.0938	2.381	19/32	0.5938	15.081
7/64	0.1094	2.778	39/64	0.6094	15.478
1/8	0.1250	3.175	5/8	0.6250	15.875
9/64	0.1406	3.572	41/64	0.6406	16.272
5/32	0.1563	3.969	21/32	0.6563	16.669
11/64	0.1719	4.368	43/64	0.6719	17.066
3/16	0.1875	4.763	11/16	0.8875	17.463
13/64	0.2031	5.159	45/64	0.7031	17.859
7/32	0.2188	5.556	23/32	0.7188	18.256
15/64	0.2344	5.953	47/64	0.7344	18.653
1/4	0.2500	6.350	3/4	0.7500	19.050
17/64	0.2656	6.747	49/64	0.7656	19.447
9/32	0.2813	7.144	25/32	0.7813	19.844
19/64	0.2969	7.541	51/64	0.7969	20.241
5/16	0.3125	7.938	13/16	0.8125	20.638
21/64	0.3281	8.334	53/64	0.8281	21.034
11/32	0.3438	8.731	27/32	0.8438	21.431
23/64	0.3594	9.128	5 5/64	0.8594	21.828
3/8	0.3750	9.525	7/8	0.8759	22.225
25/64	0.3906	9.922	57/64	0.8996	22.622
13/32	0.4063	10.319	29/32	0.9063	23.019
27/64	0.4219	10.716	59/64	0.9219	23.416
7/16	0.4375	11.113	15/16	0.9375	23.813
29/64	0.4531	11.509	61/64	0.9531	24.209
15/32	0.4688	11.906	31/32	0.9688	24.606
31/64	0.4844	12.303	63/64	0.9844	25.003
1/2	0.5000	12.700	1	1.0000	25.400

New Ham Commandment II

Thou shalt not covet thy neighbor's rig......You could spend, or possibly waste, a fortune on a rig, antenna, or accessory "just like Elmer's," only to discover that his choice of what he does with the hobby is completely different from what turns you on. Look around, read the journals, pick up a used rig and learn how to use it, listen to what's going on locally and around the world. Consider the advice herein and in other reliable sources, then try out the nifty stuff at hamfests, fellow amateur's stations, and "on approval" purchase. You're likely to have a ball doing it, and the hard-earned bucks will go a lot further!

Routing and Grounding Cables

There are many ways to route coax and other cables between antennas and operating areas, and the method you choose will have a definite bearing on your safety and that of your station and home.

Let's assume that you've properly seen to the grounding of the tower or other antenna support and you are ready to connect your station to the world. Connectors are in place on the cables and you're ready to hike up to the feed point. We won't tell you how to climb the tower or the ladder safely. We're interested in the welfare of the cables here, and assume that you are smart enough to protect yourself!

Set up the cables on the ground on a reel or with a helper who can dispense them without tangles or kinks. Today's hi-tech coaxes can be ruined in an instant by careless installation procedures.

Start at the top

At the feed point, be it on a tower, in a tree, on a pole, or at the end of a rope, you are faced with a termination, which is probably a female connector or simple nut and screw terminals. Your cable, prepared accordingly to match, should first be held in place temporarily with tape, providing plenty of slack so the connections can be made without strain or risk.

There are several things to consider here:

Will the cable be supported at this point only, such as with a telescoping or crank-up tower or the center of a dipole supported only at its ends? If so, provision for its support by other means than the antenna feed point should be considered. With a tower and cables of RG 8 size or greater, grips of the "Chinese finger puzzle" type[1] are ideal.

 They can easily support over 100 feet of cable with no strain on the connector, *but they must be installed* **before** *the connector.* This is also a convenient place to

---

[1] *Kellems* brand are well known. See p/n **700,A,B,C**

make a 360 degree loop in the coax above the support device, about 4 to 8 inches in diameter (bigger coax – bigger loop) as a lightning stopper[2] The same principles apply to a dipole, but ideally, *no dipole should be unsupported in the center for ideal performance, even with a lightweight coaxial cable[3] feed line*.

Things are a bit different for crank-ups and telescoping towers, and methods abound. We are partial to full support at the top and guide rings all the way down. Rings need to be clean and polished for zero abrasion to the cable, and, ideally, the cables should be polyethylene jacketed for maximum lubricity. A surplus, full size, plastic barrel or drum with drain holes, elevated on cement blocks and secured is good for down position storage. Properly placed, the cable will usually train itself to spiral in, and thus the risk of damage due to kinking or tight bends is minimized.

Moving on down

Securing the cables to a fixed tower can be accomplished with good quality electrician's tape. Several turns around only the tower leg will provide a protective pad for the cable when included in the next 3-4 turns in a fairly wide

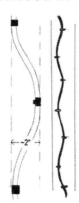

pattern. The tape should be snug, but must never be so tight as to alter the shape of the cable. Repeat the procedure every 3-4 feet to the ground or point of direction change. Wide, UV resistant plastic ties or hook and loop tape are also good if a pad is used around the

tower leg to protect the coax. ←

Routing on a pole is best done with single-nail plastic wire guides of a size that will not

---

[2] See Lightning hints in Chapter 5
[3] See "The Ubiquitous Dipole" in Chapter 8.

compress the cable when nailed. The placement should be every three feet in a very slight serpentine path, so the strain is spread evenly throughout the downward path.

Back on terra firma

At the bottom of the tower or pole a variety of options are possible. A sampling might include:

1. No junction, just a change in direction in a cable, from vertical to horizontal, the latter being above, on, or in the earth. Another simple 360-degree loop is a simple and effective lightning safety device (see bottom of page)- lightning doesn't like to change direction—or rather, lightning is too powerful to be turned around a corner. The loop is worth doing, no matter what other measures one might employ.

2. A complete break in the line allowing a change from hard line to coax, remote switch, or lightning devices.

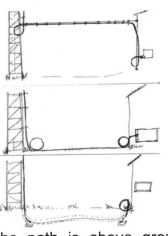

←Grounding blocks are available to handle multiple runs, and are an excellent procedure to follow at the base of a tower or pole. If remote switching is involved at this point, the installation instructions should be followed to the letter as regards grounding. Simply mating the same or different styles of cable can be accomplished easily by providing a plate attached to the tower or pole ground with holes to accommodate bulkhead-type, feed through, double female adapters which are easily weatherproofed.

Into the home stretch

The run from this point to the shack depends on the distance involved, and whether the route is above, on, or under the ground. If the path is above ground for any distance, the cable(s) should go back up the tower to a safe, interference-free height from which point it can be supported by a "messenger" wire which is clamped to the tower or pole ground as if it were an electrical connection, secured at the house end at the same height, and then continued to the station ground rod.

For a ground level run, a cable should have a jacket such as polyethylene for high abrasion resistance and the greatest permeability to moisture. The risk of damage by lawn and gardening equipment, critters and kids must be considered, as well as personal injury from tripping over the cable.

Underground, out of sight and mind, is always an excellent choice where feasible. See **"Bury it,"** next section, for full information as to how to do it right.

Tip: Cable from a roof or chimney antenna across a rooftop is usually subjected to extreme solar heat and abrasion if not protected. One solution is a "runner" of 1 X 2 inch wood, alkyd painted to match the roof, held in place with just a few rust-proof deck screws with a dollop of roofing caulk or cement between wood and roof to avoid leaks. The cable(s) are tied to the board with enough *wide, UV resistant* plastic ties to hold them on top. Use a board long enough to reach beyond the eave or gutter to provide a gently curved path back to the house wall.

Into the shack

If you chose the underground route in a tube or pipe, it would be nice to keep on going underground, leaving another ground rod (or two for a big gun) right at the point of entry, from which a heavy copper buss or ribbon runs through the same hole in the wall (outside of the tube) to a grounding block or termination bulkhead[4]. With the pipe sealed in place, you would now have a great, weatherproof place from which to ensure that the pipe is moisture free. Be sure it extends into the basement an inch or two so you can hang a bucket on it if condensate appears! This also a great termination point for the station ground, and one more spot to ground the coax braid before getting to the operating area.

---

[4] Don't forget the outdoors run to the service neutral from these ground rod(s) with heavy, solid copper wire (see page 95 and 99).

Any further devices for dealing with lightning that you may choose to deploy should also be here.

An above ground entry to the shack is similar to what's done at the base of the tower or pole. As before, we recommend the loop we've described earlier. It's a bargain you can't beat. Also popular are grounded panels with bulkhead connectors so that the cables can be completely disconnected at time of risk.Suggested configurations are sketched here, and a typical model is pictured below .

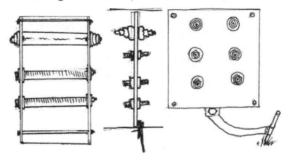

This approach is excellent, since the equipment becomes isolated, but often is not carried far enough. The lines from the outside need to be shorted to ground when not connected to the equipment. This avoids arcing at the bulkhead and provides excellent charge dissipation by the antennas and other hardware. This can be accomplished by shorted push-on connectors, singly or ganged. This would also be a reminder to unplug the gear from the wall!

Views of a copper and brass panel assembly ready for installation in a copper-lined tunnel through the wall of a ham shack. Provision is made for five coax cables, one rotor cable, and one balanced line (or two single wire leads).

Two inch copper ribbons provide an indoor braid "sandwich point and an outdoor run to a ground rod.

An approach at stations where the cables are continuous at entry is a buss of shorted and grounded connectors at the operating site, where cables may be easily removed from equipment and plugged in to ground via simple quick-disconnects. The isolation and dissipation function is easy and obvious (See drawing – page 5.11).

Rotor control cables should not be overlooked. A disconnect at the control device in the shack, with alternate mating to a jack with all conductors grounded, will isolate the device and divert induced or strike currents to ground.

The last stop

The very popular in-line arrestors on the market in the $15 to $50 price range (example below) are all effective *to some degree, directly related to how well the whole station is protected.* Installed correctly right at the equipment's RF input port, they can divert voltage spikes that enter or slip by everything else you have done from top to bottom, **but to count on them as the station's only protection would be like putting a dollar in a slot machine.** Notice the recommended size of the drain wire to ground on these devices, and consider the amperage it could handle as opposed to the average 18,000 amp lightning bolt!

Take a good look at your **whole** station, your pride and joy, and think what nature's power could do to it, the whole QTH, and the living inhabitants. Also, Chapter 5 (Lightning) is well worth your scrutiny and your serious attention!

Also worth a look is the I.C.E. line of lightning protection devices. Check them out on our website.

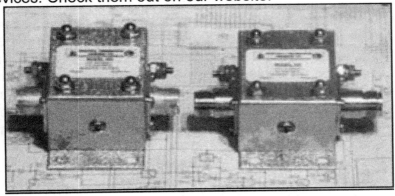

Bury it!

There are many reasons why the wires and cables to and from an amateur radio shack to the antennas and related equipment would be better off underground:

1. Consider the aesthetics. Bad enough that an ugly tower (in the eyes of the neighbors, of course!) sits in the middle of the yard, without a maze of wire hanging, lying and running to the house, making the place look like a city utility jungle in the 20's!

2. How about the risk? The precious line can be laid in the grass where it can be destroyed by mowers, aerators, gophers, and golf shoes. It can be strung from tower/pole via one or more poles to the shack for the squirrels and birds to romp on, the sun to fry, the weight of snow and ice to stretch and the wind to whip.

3. And then there is lightning. One does not have to be a genius to know that all of that copper wire is safer underground than exposed to the perils above. All lightning protection is based on sending current to ground, no matter what it has to run through, so why offer a path if you don't absolutely have to?

So let's bury it!

Break out the pick and shovel, rent a trencher and open a nice ditch, throw in the cable(s) and cover it up, right? Right, but here are a few fine points:

Choose the right cable.

There are many levels of specifications for cables designed for direct burial. Included in them are headings such as permeability, armor, water blocking, pressurization, lineal strength, and temperature operating range. Perhaps the most common buriable cable we see is telephone service line. Typically, it consists of two or more pairs of PVC insulated, solid bare copper wire, lightly held together with a fiber tape or strand, flooded with a sticky, moisture-blocking material, and covered with a copper or aluminum alloy shield or "armor." This core is flooded with more of the sticky stuff as a polyethylene jacket is applied to complete the package. In use, when the cable is opened at an end, the conductors are separated and connected where required, and the shield is connected to ground. The tough and highly impermeable jacket wards off stone, rodent or other puncture damage. The flooding compound oozes out at the open end and through any damage, preventing moisture from entering.

Basically, buriable coax should and would have similar features. A side effect is cost. It is obvious that such a cable will cost more than one of standard construction. A simpler solution can do an excellent job for the amateur, at a decent price if the site is fairly dry earth or sand, without sharp rock debris. Heavy polyethylene jacket alone is very moisture impermeable, tough and scuff resistant enough to do the job for many years. *Regular (Class I) or non-contaminating (Class II) PVC) should never be buried directly, alone or with other cables.* These polyvinyl chloride jackets are subject to tiny pinholes, too small to see, but a problem under pressure. Further, they are more moisture permeable than polyethylene, and will eventually fail if directly buried. Therefore, if the path is through the "dismal swamp," pond or river, plan on the double whammy, a coax with both the polyethylene jacket <u>AND</u> the moisture blocking compound.

Remember, anyone can advertise a cable as a "**direct burial**" type, but **unless it has the characteristics that will** make it survive in <u>any</u> "in the earth" environment for 20 or more years, it falls into the same class as your dog's bone!

How many cables?

Most amateurs run more than one or 2 cables out to the antenna from the shack. Indeed, some have a bundle of feed and service lines as big as a fire hose! (See page 76)

Does the path run through a nice lawn?

If so, slit an outline of the trench through the sod and turn the strip of sod upside down on the lawn. When the trench is re-filled and tamped, lay the sod back and wet it down – you're an instant hero! Even better, plan to do it when the family is away for the day!

Consider a tube or pipe.

With any number beyond 1 or 2 it is a good idea to bury a tube for the cables plus a pulling rope. This puts it all out of sight and provides for new runs and replacements at any time with ease by simply preparing the new line(s) and a new piece of rope and pulling them through with the old rope and any line requiring replacement. If the pull is more than 10 feet, it pays to use electrician's pulling lubricant to minimize friction and seizing damage. A professional pulling grip is a great accessory if you do this often with multiples.

The tube is simple, and actually almost free, if one considers the premium price of true direct-bury cables compared to standard types plus the pipe cost.   Select the tube. Schedule 40 PVC in the 20 foot lengths with "belled" ends is the best, but, since there is no pressure in the pipe, the "thin wall," drain type will do very well if you use common sense and care with the back filling phase of the job.

A no-brainer:

Perforated sewer or drainpipe is NOT recommended as a conduit for cable. It will allow moisture to both exit and enter, plus abrasive grit, roots, and critters, none of which are good company for any or all cables.

How big?

Count your cables and select the size you need. How? Cut short pieces of cables of the sizes you're using, trot down to the hardware store and lay them in a piece of pipe. The right pipe size is the one you see **half full.** If you have any doubts or possible future plans, go larger!

The next picture shows a cross section of 2 inch and 1.5 inch conduit with an assortment of cables including 8X, RG8, and 0.590 inch coaxes, a rotor cable and 3/16 double weave pulling ropes, illustrating suggested usage. This size of rope is over-kill for strength, but a better choice than the small rope that can cut through cable jackets when pulling.

Do it right!

The tube must be buried properly to avoid having standing water from condensation, which is inevitable, or flooding. The easiest way do the job is to dig the trench as deep as the hard freeze line plus the outside diameter of the pipe, and assemble the complete run of pipe or tube on the ground beside the trench, with the cable(s) and rope inside. At a point where the pipe will head toward the surface at each end, dig a hole <u>at least</u> as big as a gallon bucket in the bottom of the trench and fill it back up to the trench bottom level with coarse sand and gravel to handle the water that collects in the pipe. Carefully lower the complete assembly into the trench with the aid of rope slings and helpers. Depending on the terrain, and using the short rope center sling, "crown" the pipe so all collected moisture <u>always</u> will run out either or both ends.

CENTER SUPPORT

If the cable route turns up at either end, prepare 90 degree **"sweeps"** (<u>not elbows</u>) by drilling a number of holes about an inch from one end on the outside of the curve and install them into the coupling on each of the pipe ends, being sure the holes open down where the moisture will pass into the sand and gravel "dry-wells" you've prepared. Better yet, a "Tee" can be used here, pointing the side opening down into the sand and/or gravel.

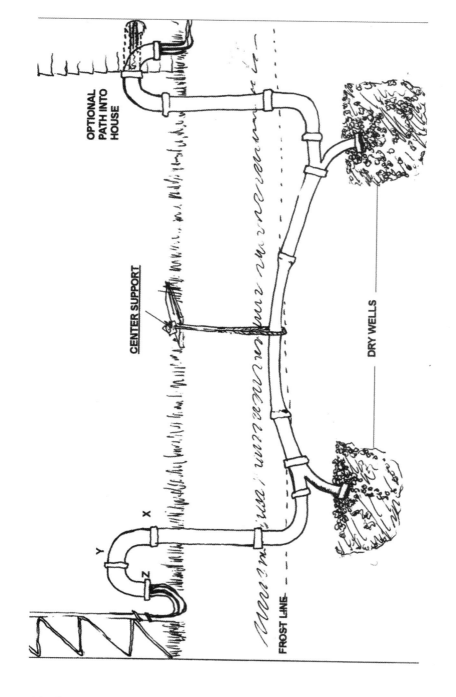

At the pole or tower end of the run, the 90-degree "sweep" is followed by a vertical straight pipe long enough to clear the ground by 2 or 3 feet. Top it off with two 90-degree "sweeps" coupled to, but not glued to, the straight pipe, making the next addition or removal of cable much easier. A coupling on the very end minimizes the likelihood of water "wicking" uphill on rainy days. The open end can be plugged with a wad of fiberglass cloth or insulation to keep out wasps and other critters, and it is easy to remove and replace when necessary.

Backfill the trench carefully, with plenty of tamping, maintaining the crowned position of the tube. Tamp along side of the tube until it is covered by about four to six inches of rock-free backfill, and then tamp or walk on it carefully to settle the area over the pipe.

At this point, since it may be impossible to know what future digging may occur in the area, a good precaution is to lay a bright red 6 inch polyethylene tape in the trench before doing the rest of the backfilling. This will, hopefully, warn future diggers that your precious line is inches below. Red indicates electrical lines, and the stuff is readily available from contractor supply houses, or a friendly electric company guy you meet at the bowling alley!

The shack end of this whole project is mainly the same, whether it's straight in, down and in, or up and in. The lightning protection scheme should be considered here, as well as the possibility of future additions or changes.

The following pictures are configurations of readily available ABS and schedule 40 PVC pipe (*Lowes, Home Depot,* etc.) used in the project as indicated.

Two 2 inch "sweeps" used as a weather-proof earth exit.

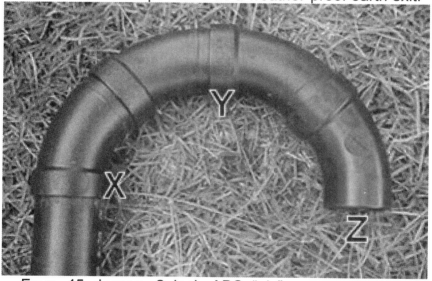

Four, 45 degree, 2 inch ABS "els" as an alternate for "sweeps." Both supply a safe bend radius for coax and are easily placed after the cables are run in the main conduit.

Detail of low end of conduit run, showing 2 inch ABS pipe into a 2 inch long turn ABS "wye" or cleanout "tee," then a 2 inch schedule 40 "sweep."

Same assembly with two 45 degree "els" instead of "sweep."

Coaxial Cable Around a Rotor

It sounds simple, but, improperly used, good coax can be ruined in a few weeks and station performance can be gradually impaired or suddenly wrecked by a poorly installed run around the rotor **WAY** up there on top of the tower.

Here are a few tips to help ensure lasting success with your setup:

Select the right coaxial cable

All "flexible" coax is not the same, nor are all of those so described suitable for service around a rotor. There are a number of top quality coaxial cables in the market advertised as *"flexible,"* referring to ease of installation. Such cable is easily routed through difficult bends and turns as a one-time operation. Once placed, it's there to stay. Even *"hard line,"* with smooth or corrugated outside wall, is considered *"flexible"* as opposed to *"rigid,"* like pipe. All of these cables have a solid center conductor that will "machine harden" or stiffen with continuous bending, making it stiff enough to migrate though the dielectric toward the shield. This causes a significant impedance bump and, ultimately, arcing, short circuiting, or complete breakage.

Stranded center conductor coaxial cable is what we refer to when **constant** movement is possible or required. The number of strands involved is dictated by the specific use of the coax. For example, the jumpers used between pieces of equipment in the station area would be likely to have 7 to 19 strand center conductors; constantly moved coax like a hand-held radio link to an outside antenna might have 19 or 26 strands; and a microphone cable on a rock concert stage, 42 or 65 or more strands.

The rest of its construction further governs the flexibility of coaxial cable. The jacket and/or dielectric can be a supple rubber or rubber-like PVC, silicone rubber, rugged polyethylene, polyurethane, Teflon®, or fiberglass. The braided shield can be a variety of sizes and layers of fine or coarse wire; a foil layer can be thick or thin, bonded or loose. The possibilities are endless.

Truly flexible coax is made to be convenient and "user friendly," OR, able to do the job without destroying itself. Coax routed around a rotor is in the latter category. Ease of handling by the installer is secondary. Typical stranding will range from 7 to 19, depending on overall gauge. *Highly flexible coax is not recommended for rotor applications due to the risk of bending damage due to sagging, risk of hanging up, and wind whip.* The general rule of thumb for minimum bending of coaxial cable is 15 times the outer diameter (OD). (for example: RG8, .405X15=6 inch OD circle or 3" radius, RG8X, .242X15=3-5/8 inch OD or about 2" radius). This applies to any bend, in installation or in use, including "goof" kinks such as incurred by dropping a hank from 50 feet while holding one end!

<u>Go for it!</u>

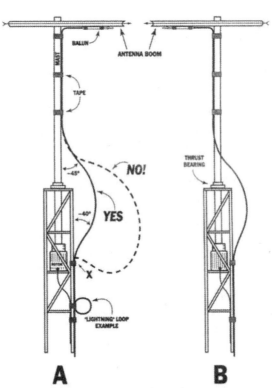

A   B

The diagram above shows the basics of an installation maximizing the life and ensuring the successful performance of any coax suitable for continuous rotor movement. When the antenna is in place, all cables are prepared with connectors and weather-proofed as required for the feed point and rotor. The rotor control should be set at mid-range with the antenna pointing in the desired direction for that setting, with all hardware properly secured. **(A)**

There are so many different types of antennas out there that it would be hard to suggest one best way to get the cables to the top of the tower or pole and attached to their end points, so we must assume that you've got that covered and a helper is at hand.

Please see the guidelines in **"Routing and Grounding,"** also in chapter 3, for proper care and handling of your precious cables.

Working from the top down, secure the rotor and coaxial cable to the tower a few feet below the rotor, allowing enough slack for the work on the mast above the rotor. If not done previously, secure the coax to the mast and boom as necessary to support it and the balun (if any). This can be done by making a few turns of good quality black vinyl electrician's tape around **only the mast or boom at the chosen point,** then including the coax in 4-6 additional turns, tight enough to hold but not to squeeze. The initial wrap makes a "pad" for the coax and protects it from abrasion by the metal member, and should be 1-2 inches wide. The final wrap

should be approximately 1/2 inch narrower.

Repeat this procedure several times on the way down the mast, the last wrap being no closer than 12-15 inches above the thrust bearing or tower top.

Complete the rotor wiring and route the rotor

cable all the way to the rotor control at ground level or at the shack, taping it here and there temporarily, for safety.

Return to the coax-routing task, choosing the tape point **(X)** at or near the top of the tower. Secure the coax temporarily. Wake up your helper whom you've carefully trained to understand the control, what it does, and how many degrees there are in a full circle. Have him or her, in constant contact with you, rotate the antenna clockwise 180 degrees or to the stop while you observe the lay of the coax. It should look like the **(B)** illustration and have made no contact with tower or other hardware on the way. Now have the helper rotate the antenna system 360 degrees, in the opposite direction or to the stop, and make the same observations. Repeat if necessary until it is perfect. Its path should **NEVER** resemble the dotted path in **(A).**

Moving down the tower, a good final step at the top is a 360 degree twelve inch loop in all cables, taped in place at four points on the loop a rung or two below the rotor. This will provide a bit of slack for adjustments, repairs, etc, and provide a simple but effective lightning arrestor. Repeat this step at the bottom of the tower and before entering the house for even more protection.

Follow the routing guide referred to above for both cables to dress and secure the cables to the tower leg or pole and get on the air! **_Reminder:_** _All tasks of this type should be logged, both initially and periodically as inspected, touched up, or repaired. Scheduled maintenance is invaluable in keeping your station on the air._

i

The Right Rotor Cable

This is another of the "top ten" subjects on the help list. It should be easy, with the manual and illustrations from the manufacturer, but we wonder at the lack of detail offered for things out of the ordinary.

The current-carrying capacity of the cable is, of course, the governing factor in choosing the cable size in relation to the distance from rotor to rotor control. If you have lost the instructions or they are incomplete for your project, check out the motor and/or brake current ratings in the specifications data and use this information to calculate your cable needs with the help of the table on our website (www.thewireman.com). There is an example there to help as well.

Consider also the load you are rotating. A monster tri-bander plus a VHF/UHF array will draw much more current than a modest quad at the same distance so lean toward the next size larger cable if you are near the suggested or calculated distance limit.

All rotors require two to three heavier wires plus 1 to 6 smaller wires which are low current indicator and control conductors. Some of the latest models have the least number of wires, one of which does the whole control and indicator job via a pulse system.

Typically, a rotor cable such as that for the popular Hy-Gain models will have two heavy wires (1 black and 1 white) and six smaller control wires (brown, red, yellow, blue, orange, and green jackets). Six wire cables, all the same gauge, are black, white, brown, blue and green, and 5 wire models have all but the blue. The pulse wire, where used, may or not be shielded and usually has a violet jacket.

Outer jackets should be as long lasting as the best coax used, for obvious reasons, and, in the case of crank-up towers, scuff-proof polyethylene is recommended.

The bottom line here is your investment in both the rotor and the cable to operate it. If there is any doubt based on the cable's capability to handle the load, either use heavier gauge wire or avoid running the rotor if the weather conditions are dicey.

For more information and details of the various cables for rotors, check out http://www.thewireman.com/rotorp.html

There is also a table on page 207 that will help in making the right choice for your installation.

New Ham Commandment III

Thou shalt not steal......Aside from the obvious, a good operator does not take free rides - If you use a local repeater regularly, contribute to its upkeep with dollars, time, or labor. If you use a net often, help with a relay now and then, make a phone call, be net control, etc. If you become active in a club, pay dues!

New Ham Commandment IV

Thou shalt not kill...... Nothing wipes out finals in solid state rigs like transmitting into no load. Be sure of your coax, connectors, antenna, switches, etc. Use a dummy load to check out the rig and tune it, and then use low power and an SWR or wattmeter to check the system before "blasting away." There are a dozen reasons why your path to the antenna could be open or shorted – from lightning to the cleaning lady, so a good operator always does a thorough "cockpit check" before taking off. Then, when you shut down, unplug, isolate, or disconnect!

Grounding a Tower

There are some basic considerations for any tower installation, whether professionally installed or the self-engineered ham job. We'll assume you have one erected and ready to use, and you would like to minimize the likelihood of losing   everything to nature's wrath in the form of lightning.

A major first step is research. Know the enemy. Lightning risk is different everywhere in the world, right down to the immediate surroundings of your neighborhood. Your local weather department, TV or radio meteorologist, county agent or library can give you the comparative strike frequency for your area. The senior neighbors around you can tell a tale of what the weather's been like over the years. Your own observations as to the terrain, elevation, nearby structures and vegetation are all factors that will help you to assay your potential risk. The next page is a map, showing the average US thunderstorm days per year in the continental US.[1] Use it to assess the relative risk at your QTH.

Please note that this article is targeted toward only the tower phase of your station. The protection of the operating equipment is considered here, but the details are discussed separately in "Station Grounding."

1. Dealing with or handling a direct strike.

Man-made structures everywhere handle the awesome power of lightning by simply providing sufficient paths to carry the load to earth. A bolt of lightning is an instantaneous charge of electricity of an estimated _average_ of 18,000 amperes, which is enough to vaporize or explode nearly anything it hits or that tries to contain it.

Consider the Empire State building in New York, which takes thousands of strikes a year with no damage. The strike current is distributed throughout the building's conductive structure and other conductors to a maze of conductors in the earth and around the base to harmless neutralization.

---

[1] Map courtesy of the National Lightning Safety Institute, Louisville, CO 80027. <www.lightningsafety.com>

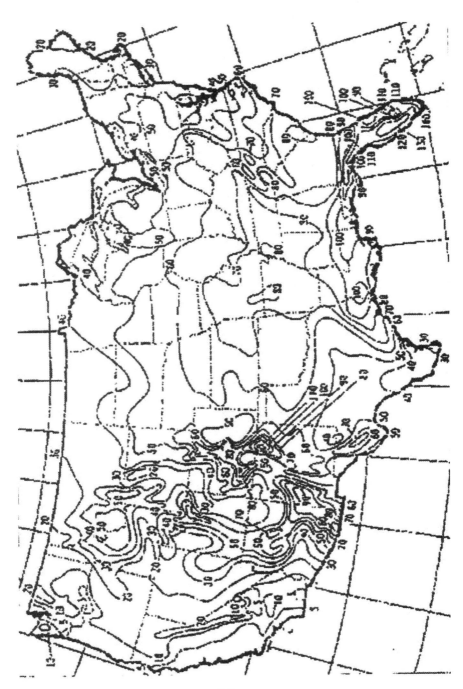

This is exactly what you want to do with your tower, to the best of your ability.

Lightning strikes follow a "leader," or ionized path to or from earth. We don't always have the means to change this, so our best hope is to disperse it as much as we can when it's path includes the tower. Since all three legs can become part of the path, we've already divided the current somewhat. You do not want the inevitable or infrequent strike to blast into the concrete base destructively, so a ground rod adjacent to each leg, right at the edge of the concrete and joined to the tower leg at a 45 degree angle with a heavy conductor will facilitate the divided path.

Better yet, when you dig the hole for the tower, drive 3 rods at the bottom of the hole near the wall, bolt or braze the heavy copper wire tightly to them[2] and run it to the top of the hole plus 6 - 8 feet. Cover this set of rods with dirt before setting the tower base prior to pouring the concrete. The wires can be "stapled" to the wall[3] to keep them out of the concrete as well..

When the tower is erected, the three wires are attached to three ground rods 2 - 6 feet away from the tower, joining all

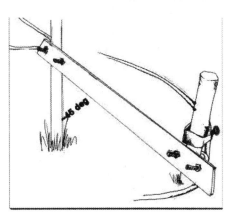

---

[2] Excellent protection for this connection, soon to be buried, is a heavy coat of automobile undercoating (from a spray can from an auto parts store).
[3] Make your own with heavy gauge galvanized wire like clothesline – a 3-5 inch "U."

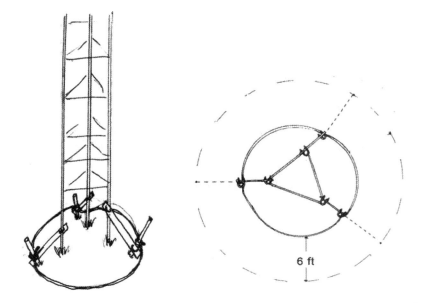

three in a circle of the same wire adding to the dispersal field. If the risk you've determined for your area is great, three more rods approximately 6 feet straight out from the first set, connected to the first three and also in a circle, would be prudent. This could, and perhaps should, be even further expanded in areas of Florida and Gulf states, on top of hills with no trees, and in open fields where the only target is your tower. The material sizes recommended are for average risk installations, and could be modified up or down according to what you know of the area's history. How this is accomplished depends on your budget, ingenuity, and determination. Copper bars, ¼ inch X 1 inch clamped with stainless steel or hot dipped galvanized "U" bolts to tower leg[4] and ground rod will handle the 45-degree path. Copper ribbon 2 by 0.020 inch is effective as well, though more difficult to clamp properly (see page 99).Solid 4 AWG copper wire is good for the first circle and the path to the second circle, where solid 6 AWG copper wire will work. A final, solid 6 AWG copper wire to the power company neutral completes the job. All of these wires should be buried at least 6 inches

---

[4] A small stainless steel sheet-metal pad can be placed between the tower leg and the copper bar or ribbon to minimize dissimilar metal galvanic action.

deep, to maximize the current dispersion capability. Conductive guy wires, if used, will further enhance the dispersal field through their anchors, which, if concrete, should be by-passed with 4 to 6 AWG solid copper wire to a ground rod adjacent to the anchor.

Note: The several drawings in this section portray the ground rods out of the ground for illustration purposes only. In practice, they should be even with or slightly below the surface. This is for personal, walk-around, safety, and, to ensure the maximum dispersal surface to the earth. This is not a place for "out of sight, out of mind," however, since all above or nearly above ground connections should be checked annually for integrity.

The ground rods used need to be long enough to reach earth with conductivity due to moisture, enhanced if necessary with mineral salts. The length can vary from less than 8 feet, to 20, or even 30 feet. Eight feet is typical. Most rods are 5/8-inch heavily copper-clad steel, although 3/4 inch hot dipped galvanized steel rods are readily available. Rods longer than 8 feet are threaded and coupled together in sections as they are buried, driven, or jetted. This type of situation is common in Florida. Getting them in the ground depends on the nature of the ground. A fence post driver or maul works well in plain old earth or light clay, but might be hopeless in rocky terrain, where drilling might be necessary, or possibly a bevy of short rods. In some cases where rock is a problem, a rod or heavy solid wire is laid in 1 or 2 foot deep trenches, tangent and/or perpendicular to the circle.

Another method: Flatten the end of a 1/2 inch water pipe to make a jet and hooking up the other end to a water hose. Use a tee and a short nipple and cap on one side and a valve on the other. Start out on a stepladder, pressing down and twisting back and forth as the jet blasts its hole.

The local scrap metal junkyard can be a great

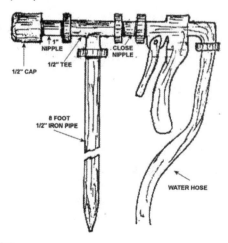

source for heavy copper bar stock and wire, at a fraction of hardware store price. The sizes suggested above are nominal. The bigger the better, but use something, even if it's temporary until you can afford better. Even stranded wire is better than nothing. It's more inductive and will vaporize quicker, but it could well last long enough to convey the destructive current to earth and save the equipment.

Another option for the various connections is brazing or "*Cadweld.™*" This is ideal, but not mandatory. Mechanical junctions, properly executed and protected are OK. Remember, the system should be inspected thoroughly at least annually and after each real, suspected, or imagined strike.

Buried lines, such as the one from the tower network to the power company neutral should be checked after a suspected strike for resistance. If higher than nominal[5] for wire of that size, it should be replaced. Many texts will state that this link is unnecessary beyond a certain distance, but this is only so if every other conductor between tower and shack is completely protected or disconnected, establishing two separate systems during a lightning event.

2. Dealing with the effects of a nearby strike.

This relates to the common ground described above as the connection of the tower ground to the power company neutral at the service entrance. This is outlined in the National Electric Code as a requirement in all electrical systems at a single address.

The reasoning is simple. Most lightning damage is not from direct strikes; rather, it occurs from a nearby hit and the subsequent surge entering your system as an elevation of the neutral potential. This allows the 220/110 differential to remain constant but the neutral can be thousands of volts higher than the earth ground potential at your station, *IF* the latter, including the tower, is not connected to the power company neutral. If common ground is absent, the destructive path, direct or induced, is via all other conductors

---

[5] Wire tables in Chapter 7 show nominal or typical resistance of any size copper wire.

between the two areas for the microsecond it takes to destroy the linked equipment. Tie it all together at the utility point of entry[6], and the surge rises and falls in unison in every conductor in/at the QTH

3. Lowering the risk of a strike.

Lightning strikes are the arc struck along an ionized path from two areas of opposite charge build-up. They are the ultimate static charge discharge spark, the same as that generated by scuffing your shoes over the rug and nearly touching the doorknob or someone else's hand. A rapid swirling of water vapor particles, a cloud, racing through the sky, causes an equal and opposite charge to build up on its bottom surface and on the surface of the earth below. The  earth charge reaches toward the cloud from every promontory such as blades of grass, tree leaves, pointed rocks, water wave crests, building peaks and corners, etc., and, of course, towers. The cloud charge reaches for the opposite polarity earth charge. In the absence of sufficient dissipation paths, "leaders" of heavy opposite charge reach out for each other, meet and create an ionized particle path, which the lightning bolt follows. Lightning rods on the house and barn, barbwire fence, grain conveyor auger assemblies, telephone poles with a spike of wire on top, towers, antennas provide sharp points that contribute to the dissipation rate. Commercial multi-point dissipaters and wire brush material like continuous point barbwire are utilized everywhere lightning is prevalent. It works! The smaller devices, we call them "Porcupines," p/n 8741 are a very popular marine accessory for tall masted sailboats and other vessels, critical industry facilities, bridges, computer operations, communications,

---

[6] *Never loosen a power company's ground clamp.* Get your own at the hardware store and add it to the utility ground wire.

and commercial and amateur radio operations in high-risk areas. They provide an area of lower risk, where deployed, by slowing the rate of charge buildup between earth and sky. This is accomplished by providing many paths for charge dissipation.

Station Grounding

Performance is the key word in station grounding – not that lightning and operating safety should be ignored, but we do look at it a bit differently. Further, there are about as many different solutions required as there are stations! The following discussion is designed to lead you through the important principles and suggest ways to get the job done.

Ideally, picture your station right on mother earth, appropriately connected to the antenna, power source, and ground rod. Practically, we'd better place the transceiver and associated equipment in the shack and run the shortest conductor possible to the ground rod. Shoot for 10 feet or less, but if longer is a must, do what is necessary. This is sometimes difficult when the radio shack is a long way from earth ground[7].

Functionally, you are supplying a counterpoise, an aid to matching, a path for stray RF and high voltage spikes to ground, and an atmospheric noise suppressor.

We're dealing mainly with RF here, so the surface area of this conductor is more important than its power-handling capacity. Typical choices might be surplus copper tubing, copper ribbon, or tinned copper braid, run without sharp corners from a point centrally located behind the radio equipment out to the ground rod. Ideally, when you go from inside to out of doors, copper ribbon or copper tubing is better than braid, since water in the braid accelerates its deterioration and alters its resistive characteristics unless it is in a tube.

The connections to the equipment from the central point behind the equipment are very important, and should not be

---

[7] Long runs to ground are discussed in the next section.

treated carelessly. They need to be tight and should not reduce the surface area of the path. Remember, it's RF. No connectors are necessary, simply full-surface handshakes (fig. 3). Fender washers are ideal and, in this instance, separate connectors or terminals (fig. 2) are a waste of time and money, and can do more harm than good. Just poke a hole in the braid (fig. 1) and make a sandwich to join two or more or go straight to the ground terminal on the equipment with a pair of fender washers.

◄ fig. 1 Simple preparation for fender washer "sandwich"

fig. 2 ► Wrong way to terminate braid in RF applications

The braid "sandwich" or "handshake" for an ideal RF ground path fig. 3

Tinned copper braid makes the best conductor from each piece of equipment to the central mating point due to its great flexibility, ample surface and ease of use, in addition to

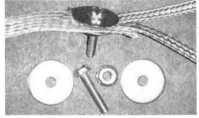

◄ Cut braid from each piece of equipment to the length of the most distant.
Attach all to a single point at the end of the copper ribbon or larger braid leading to the outside ground rod. ►

making housekeeping less of a chore (you do dust every so often, don't you?). Radial paths of nearly equal length, like

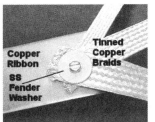

Copper Ribbon
SS Fender Washer
Tinned Copper Braids

the branches of a tree to the central point, are the most efficient way to complete the job.

◄ Picture illustrates the braid or ribbon sandwich technique for the start of the path from central point to ground rod.

There is a great temptation to establish a ground buss at the rear of the operating area as a neat way to ground everything. Unfortunately, it is close to "daisy-chaining" the equipment and can cause "ground loops" (several RF signals in the same path in the same or opposite direction). Buss-bar systems can be quite expensive as well, and the many terminations can be a source of noise if they are not tight. Ground busses are more appropriate as a handy DC ground on a test or experiment bench, not related to RF transmission and receiving.

The connection to a ground rod is also a point for full surface contact, as shown here. This is a task that is easily handled with a vise, tin shears, and drill plus a pair of brass or stainless steel nuts and bolts. The same technique is useful in attaching ribbon to a round tower leg, but a stainless steel shim or chemical

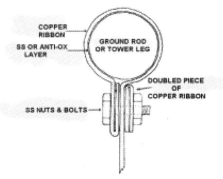

COPPER RIBBON
SS OR ANTI-OX LAYER
GROUND ROD OR TOWER LEG
DOUBLED PIECE OF COPPER RIBBON
SS NUTS & BOLTS

◄ should be placed between a galvanized steel leg and the copper to avoid dissimilar metal interaction.

Finally, a reminder that must be repeated after each discussion of grounding of any kind: The ground rod installed near the shack should be connected to the power company neutral at the service entry to the house. This connection should be with a heavy (4 to 6 AWG solid copper) wire run along the foundation, outside and at or just below the surface. This is "common ground," which is discussed elsewhere in this chapter. Don't ignore it. It could save your house, its contents, and your life.

In the previous section, dissipation was mentioned as a useful feature in lightning protection. You can add to this protection by utilizing your antennas as dissipaters when you are not operating. The drawing below illustrates a simple method for doing this with minimal cost. Although the various antenna switches for this purpose are a bit more convenient, they cannot beat the degree of positive isolation for your precious equipment gained by this method. Again, remember to unplug when your station is not operating or at risk.

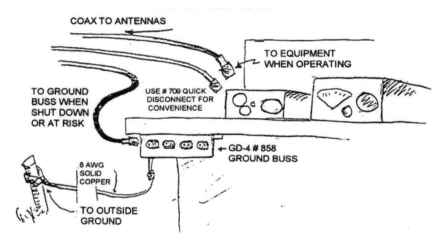

Second story station grounding

Long runs from station to ground can present problems to good station operation when the distance approaches or exceeds a quarter wavelength. Usually the problem appears at a specific frequency as feedback or blanking and can be most irritating if it interferes with one or more of your favorite operating frequencies.

The protection features of your setup require a good ground and you should not operate without one. A good RF system calls for a large surface like that described in the previous section, and the most practical way from the second story is usually down along the outside wall to a ground rod at the earth surface. The ground rod is then also linked to the utility ground at the earth ground at the electric meter via 6 AWG or larger solid bare copper, completing the safety protocol.

The long conductor from station to ground rod can be 3/8" or larger copper tubing or pipe, flattened and drilled at each end for attachment to ground rod and copper ribbon or braid at the top. Check the local junk yard or used building materials yard first, then refrigeration people (used copper tubing is usually never re-used). The cost will be half that you'll see at the hardware store. The pipe or tubing, cleaned up and painted, will be inoffensive on the house.

Alternately, one-inch or wider copper ribbon or open-mesh copper wire such as run from lightning rods will do the job as well, if available. Ribbon and/or tinned copper braid are used to complete the inside job in the station area, as described earlier.

This gets the job done for RF and lightning safety, but does not cover the problems possible due to length. The long ground line acts like an antenna in the worst way, by presenting a reactance in conflict with your operating frequency at some point.

Possible solutions include a switchable dual ground of shorter length just hanging out of the window to compromise the RF problem, connecting a ground lead to nearby plumbing, using no ground, and operating into balanced line through a tuner. All of these put safety at risk as regards lightning.

The "Artificial Ground" devices on the market are basically simple tuners capable of supplying a canceling reactance where necessary, and as such, can be most valuable in keeping your station happy when ground is a long way from the rig.

Do not, however, use such a device in lieu of a true low resistance path that will handle a surge or spike of power due to lightning.

Some tips on Lightning Protection From the Experts

Some of the following repeat some of the comments in The Wirebook, but they are important enough for seconds, especially since they come mostly from our friends at *INDUSTRIAL COMMUNICATION ENGINEERS, LTD. (ICE)*.

1. Always bring coaxial cables to ground level before entering the equipment area. This includes all radio shacks, even those on the second or higher floor.

2. Ground shields at <u>every</u> opportunity, from antenna to shack, using the shortest possible conductor to earth terminal. As much as 80% of a strike or induced current comes in on the shield.

3. Use blocking-type lightning arrestors as a final line of defense for sensitive equipment in the shack after doing everything right en route from the antenna. Gas tube-only types are a waste.

4. Create your shack as close to ground (or below) as possible at an outside wall and establish a bulkhead grounding system at the point of entry and as close to earth ground as possible to ensure maximum protection and minimum risk.

5. Forget water pipes as lightning or RF grounds, even if they appear to be totally metallic.

6. Try to bundle control (rotor, etc) lines together but separate from coaxial cable(s) bundles. Don't forget arrestors and disconnects on these as well, and the "ground and back up" routing – same importance as coax.

7. Use a 3 step procedure on all outdoor ground connections: (a)–Insert stainless separators and/or anti-oxidant compound in/and on the connection before firmly tightening. (b)–Weather-seal the connection with patching tar or auto-undercoat spray, etc. (c)–Inspect and touch up yearly.

8. Use conductor sizes relative to what comes before, such as #4 copper or larger from a tower leg to ground rod, then #6 or larger for the 3 rod circle, etc. Solid is best, stranded is OK if jacketed, and the shorter the better– always!

If you are in a high lightning risk area and would like to consider extreme protection practice, let us know and we'll lead you to W4JTL's deep coverage article of December 2000.

At this halfway point, it's quiz time. An easy test – True or False.

The length of coax as a feedline to a properly tuned antenna is critical for optimum performance.
T/F

"N" connectors are always a better choice for best performance.
T/F

Coaxial cable lifetime ratings begin when it is put to use.
T/F

RF connectors not made the US are always suspect, and all of the famous US brands are made in the USA.
T/F

Coaxial cable of Military Specification Class IIA with non-contaminating PVC jacket is designed for direct burial applications.
T/C

Gold plated RF connectors are the very best for RF performance.
T/F

Answers at bottom of page 103

Chapter 6 Balanced Transmission Line

New Ham Commandment V

Thou shalt not worship unauthorized frequencies......Stay away from band edges beyond your license, and remember that your signal is wider than the needle on the meter. You've worked hard for your license, now bloom where you're planted!

New Ham Commandment VI

Thou shalt not worship false gods......The rules and regulations for the hobby govern power limits and width of signal. There are those out there who think that they are above such rules, and that their signal and their QSO or contest contact is the most important on the air. These scofflaws are plentiful enough, unfortunately. There is no glory in emulating them.

Answers to "Halfway Quiz"
All False

Ladder Line

Prior to the advent of coaxial cable, balanced transmission line was the only choice for amateurs. Today, many years later, balanced line is once again popular and gaining rapidly as the best choice for the well-informed HF operator as the lowest loss and most cost effective transmission line available for most amateur stations.

Actually, it is amazing to me that so many amateurs use coax as their feedline for any antenna other than beams for any HF band. Take a minute to look at the loss graph page 41 at 30 MHz, where all of the "Window" type ladderline shows a loss of 0.2 dB per 100 feet. Now note the three items that are lower: 12 AWG open ladder line, 1.25 inch hardline, LMR 1700, 7/8 inch hardline and LMR 1200!! The only item being less than a 2 dollars per foot is a ladderline! The only coaxes in the same price range as the ladderline have 4 to 5 times more loss!

Performance-wise, there is no feedline made that can, with the aid of a good tuner and an inexpensive good size wire dipole or loop, work the world at any frequency from 1 to 30 Mhz without an amplifier.

Any doubts? Consider this from Chapter 1 of *REFLECTIONS II* by W2DU, Walt Maxwell:-- page 1-2:

"Open Wire Versus Coax Feedlines

The theory behind the transmission of power through a feed line with minimum loss by eliminating all reflections and terminating the line with a perfect match is equally valid, of course, for open-wire and coaxial lines. But, in the days of open-wire lines prior to our widespread use of coax, theory was tempered with practical considerations. Open-wire line was, and still is, used with high SWR to obtain tremendous antenna flexibility relative to operating power over a wide range of frequencies with high efficiency. This is because all power reflected from the feed line-to-antenna mismatch which reaches the input source is conserved, not dissipated. The power is returned to the antenna by re-reflection in the antenna tuner (transmatch) at the line input. But, although the loss from reflections and high SWR is not zero, this additional loss is negligible because of the low attenuation of open-wire line. If the line were loss-less (zero attenuation), no loss whatever would result because of reflections.(This is discussed further in Chapter 6, in connection with Figure 6 – 1 of REFLECTIONS II).

The error in our thinking, that standing waves on coaxial line must always be completely eliminated, originated quite naturally because the permissible reflection and SWR limits are much lower than they are in open-wire lines. When using coax for truly single-frequency operation, it makes sense to match the load and line to the degree economically feasible. But, it makes no sense to match at the load in many amateur applications where we are chiefly interested in operating over a whole band of frequencies! Single frequency operators, we are not, except as our misguided concern over increasing SWR restricts our departure from the resonant frequency of the antenna.

Many authors are responsible for perpetuating the unscientific and erroneous viewpoint that the coax-fed antenna must be operated at its self-resonant frequency. They have continually over emphasized the necessity for the antenna to be matched to the line within some arbitrary, low SWR value to preserve transmission efficiency and by implying that efficiency equals 100 minus percent reflected power. The viewpoint is wrong and unscientific because it neglects the most important factor in the equation for determining efficiency -- line attenuation. It is also erroneous because efficiency does not relate to reflected power by simple subtraction. Setting an SWR limit alone for this purpose is meaningless because the amount of reflected power actually lost is not dependent on SWR alone. The attenuation factor for the specific feed line must also be included. This is because the only reflective power lost is the amount dissipated in the line because of attenuation -- the remainder returns to the load. Some authors have so wrongly conditioned us concerning what happens to the reflected power that many of us have overlooked the correct approach to the subject. It is clearly presented in both *The ARRL Handbook* and *The Antenna*

Book that transmissions efficiency is a two - variable function of both mismatch and line attenuation with this knowledge, and by making a graph of the function appearing in *The ARRL Handbook*, presented here as Figure 1 – 1, the amateur can determine how much efficiency he will lose for a given SWR with the attenuation factor of each specific feed line. He can then decide for himself what the realistic SWR limit   should   be."

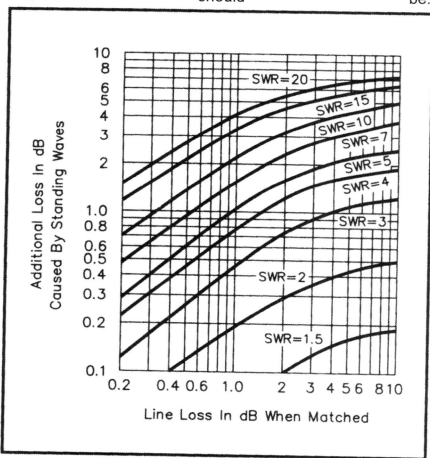

Line Loss In dB When Matched

Line loss is either from a table such as page 41 or test procedure, either way, in a matched situation. For example, if the coax feedline has a characteristic 100 foot loss of 2 dB at 2 meters with an SWR of 1.5 when matched, the added loss due to that length is no more than 0.1 dB.

Ladder Line got its name from the similarity of its construction to that of rope ladders. "True" ladderlines of quality were "homebrew" creations. The commercial models were great performers as well, utilizing plastic dividers (i.e. "rungs") that supported the parallel conductors. Unfortunately, the dividers couldn't stand much wind and/or sun and they would fail, often in less than a year.

Window style balanced line supports its conductors with a plastic web or ribbon with cut out "windows," and was a major improvement in longevity and ease of use. The velocity factor was lowered several percentage points to about 91%, almost imperceptibly increasing the signal loss.

The earlier models used 18 AWG, solid, 19% copper clad steel (CCS) conductors clad in a polyvinyl chloride (PVC) ribbon of rather poor quality, in that most of it was not very ultra-violet (UV) resistant. In the mid 1980's, the growing amateur-driven demand dictated the use of 30 % CCS and a UV resistant, tough, polyethylene jacket, which was a major improvement. At about the same time, **The Wireman** supplied the wire for a *stranded* 18-gauge model. The stranded version was very successful and so popular that 16 gauge and then 14 gauge models were born. A similar story was written for 300-ohm "window" line in 18 and 20 gauge.

The only way that the manufacturer could afford to do this on a relatively low volume operation was to use the same machinery for all of the "450's", modifying the extrusion orifices but not the width set.

Obviously, then, as the wire gauge became larger, the characteristic impedance crept down from the original design of 450 ohms, making the 14 gauge version under 400 ohms. This is very seldom a problem, for two reasons:

1. The majority of the amateur usage is not sensitive to specific impedance, since, as a balanced transmission line, a transmatch or tuner and balun are employed.

2. To make new equipment to do a true 450 ohms impedance series of products is very cost prohibitive. The dollar write-off over the volume produced would have made it cost more than the amateur market would like to pay. The designers and builders who require critical imped-

ance values (re:G5RV, W5GI, etc. antennas) have only to alter length to suit, and a purist could still "roll his own." The amateur community is still afflicted by the "...*if a little is good, more must be better*" disease, so, much of the 14 and even 16 gauge stuff is popular even though gross over-kill for its planned use. This is a hobby, however, so there isn't too much wrong with the, "if it feels good, do it" attitude.

Making it work

The successful promise and use of ladderline does require a little effort. It's not as simple to install as coax. Keeping the "balanced" concept in mind is the secret formula. At any given point in its path, the wave form of the signal on the two conductors is equal in magnitude, opposite in polarity, and thus self-canceling, unless its pretty figure 8 pattern is distorted by an undesired reaction to a nearby RF conductor, field, or reflector. We'll add two points to this: **performance and common sense**. Naturally we want the best performance possible from the antenna, and the transmission line routing plays a major part. We will outline an ideal procedure for the task, but you must apply the common sense, since everyone's QTH is different. What works for you is what's best for you. Think about the fact that what you are installing is equal in loss performance to 7/8 inch hard line at 1/25th of the price!! That should make it worth the extra effort!

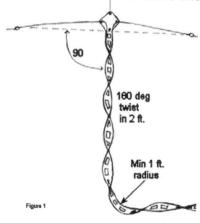

90

180 deg
twist
in 2 ft.

Min 1 ft.
radius

Figure 1

Putting it together

Starting at the antenna, the ideal route for this or any transmission line is straight away from the antenna's feed point at a right angle (90 degrees) to each antenna leg. This, in the case of a dipole for example would be an imaginary straight line from the two outer ends of the dipole.

The ladderline, especially the window type, should be given a gentle twist along the way. 180 degrees in approximately two feet will help avoid self-destruction due to wind-whipping and will minimize field distortion as the line runs past trees, gutters, etc. Note also that the changes in direction should not be in a path with a radius less than 12 inches (fig.1, page 108). At some point along the way, some support of the line will

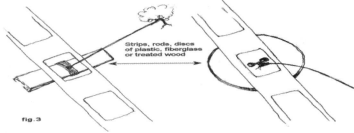

Strips, rods, discs of plastic, fiberglass or treated wood

fig.3

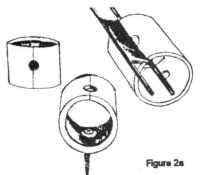

likely be necessary. Again, it needs to be isolated from other transmission lines, all metal, and all living vegetation. Stand-offs of plastic, porcelain, wood, rope, fiberglass, etc., can be "home brewed" or bought. A number of them are shown in figs. 2a (p/n 811) & 2b), and with a little imagination, you will come up with more.

Figure 2a

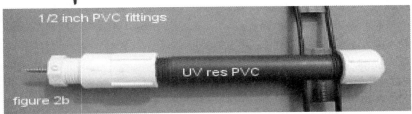

1 /2 inch PVC fittings

UV res PVC

figure 2b

Rope, such as the popular UV resistant black polyester (3/32 inch), threaded through the cutouts in the ladderline, is often used for support and routing. **This procedure is not a good idea, because, when wet, tuning will be affected and the normal RF radiation pattern will be distorted, increasing the chances for RFI and hurting performance.**

Two approaches to the job on towers are shown next. Stand-offs along a leg is one example. The drawing in fig. 4 shows a PVC tee of a size with an inside diameter close to the OD of a tower leg, halved along the long axis and fitted with two stainless worm drive clamps. It may be neces-sary,depending on the Tee's style, to file a flat notch on the surface to keep the clamp from slipping. Here's one you can make with a trip to a hardware store-not cheap but effective.

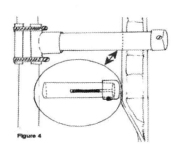

Figure 4

Another simple ready made stand-off for any size pole or tower leg is shown here — (p/n 811A)

Figure 5

We also like fig.5) because it has the least ef-fect on the RF pat-tern in any kind of weather. The out-riggers are fabricated from treated wood or fiberglass with a slit near the outer end with a plastic nut and bolt to firmly clamp the

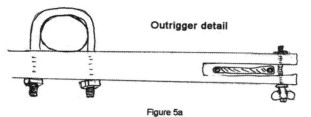

Outrigger detail

Figure 5a

ladder line. The lower out-rigger is pivoted at a third of the way back and tied or spring-loaded to keep the vertical ladder line taught.

The general path to the shack should consist of gentle turns if required, at least one foot above ground, and again, at least 6 inches away from anything conductive, inductive, reflective or living. Also worth considering is the pedestrian path!

Many amateurs are dissuaded from running balanced line into the house in fear of RF in the shack due to the un-shielded conductors. Remember though, that the radiation field around balanced line is self-canceling if undisturbed by nearby metal, other cable, or anything that has an effect on RF.

Last stop on the way to the shack is often a lightning ar-restor, or even a second one in very high risk areas. This would be, for example, at the bottom of a tower and near the ground just before entrance to the shack. There are several available for balanced line, installable on ground rods(page116), entrance panels, tower bases, etc (see I.C.E. products on <www.thewireman.com>). Manual dis-connects and switches are also utilized as an added precau-tion or seasonal shutdown protocol. See the next section for more detail and illustrations for the trip into the shack..

Proper isolation and routing will minimize stray RF. Ide-ally, the line will go straight to a tuner or matchbox. Tempo-rarily, the line can run right through a window opening in a sandwich of thick (4+ inch) foam rubber while operating and be thrown back out and grounded when idle. The same pro-cedure is possible through walls with the ladder line itself, bare or insulated wire.

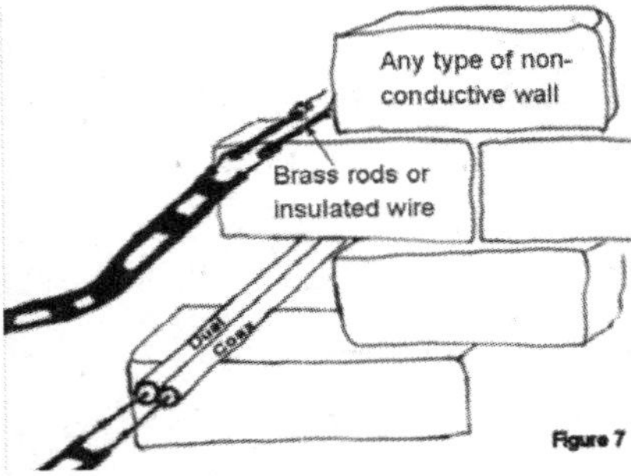

Any type of non-conductive wall

Brass rods or insulated wire

Figure 7

Permanent routing has many possibilities: The mortar be-tween 2 bricks or 2 blocks can be drilled and chiseled out to make a slot.Two small holes (1/4" or less) can be drilled through any non-conductive wall side by side about an inch apart to accommodate two insulated 14-gauge wires, which can be spliced to ladder line on either side of the wall. Either way the holes should be caulked or sealed when finished (fig. 7.)

Dual coax (50 or 75 ohm) of high % shielding and good jacket are another approach to bringing in the balanced line.

This may look like adding a big impedance bump in the line right out of the tuner, but if kept as short as possible (under 10 feet), it is a small one when compared to the full length of ladder line to the antenna. Consider this: The tuner is looking at a complex system here, with a wide range of reactance, so a few feet of twin coax is of little consequence as long as the balance remains. Run two equal length coaxes from tuner to ladder line. The two center conductors are spliced to the two ladder line conductors. The coax braid at the splice ends is

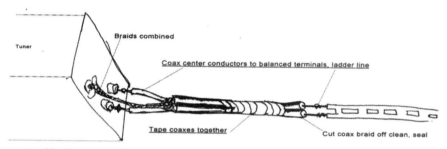

cut off clean and attached to nothing. The whole connection is then weather sealed. Inside the shack, the two center conductors are connected to the balanced feed terminals of the tuner, and both braids are joined and attached to the tuner chassis. The two coaxes are dressed by pairing with a few pieces of tape, shrink tube or spiral loom.

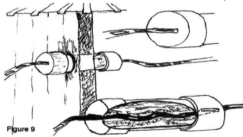

Figure 9

Any wall containing metal foil or foil-covered insulation, metal studs, utility pipes, or electrical wiring or raceways should be treated as a metal wall, both for making holes and routing transmission lines. A handy way through a metal wall (fig. 9) is through a piece of lightweight, 4-inch PVC sewer pipe, and 2 caps with slits. They are installed in the wall and caulked or sealed in place when the job is complete.. The ladder line is spiraled as previously defined, centered by wrapping it in clean, dry fiberglass type insulation and sliding it into the tube, weatherproofed, insulated, and bug-proofed.

Most tuners nowadays have built-in baluns due to the growing popularity of balanced transmission lines, but if not,

Figure 10

there are a number of ways to include one in the system. At the outer wall, the balun can be attached to or hung from a bracket on the wall. The balanced line can be attached as shown and a 10-foot (maximum) or less length of coaxial cable such as RG213/U, runs in to the tuner. This "extends" the tuner chassis out to the balun through a shielded conduit - the coax (fig. 10).

Also, one can be attached to or "hung" right on the back

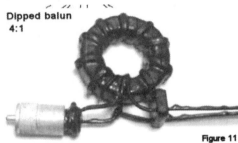

Dipped balun
4:1

Figure 11

of a tuner chassis (fig.11) or you can use an inexpensive kit to build a balun yourself and attach iot to an un-balanced SO239 port. The balun's balanced output is simply spliced to the incoming ladderline.

Other ways to "skin the cat?" Of course, that's what the hobby is all about! One idea leads to another and still another and then we share them. No other hobby is better equipped to do so!

Before moving on - what does this balun do? Actually, it does two things: First, it makes the obvious transformation of balanced to unbalanced(or vice versa) and second, it centers the tuners capability, which may or may not be necessary, depending on the tuning range of the tuner or matchbox and the type of antenna.

<u>Care and Maintenance of ladderline</u>

Cleaning and then waxing it every year or so depending on your environment easily minimizes the minor inconvenience of reactance change and increased loss due to water and dirt. Use spray or wipe-on wax just like for your car, to the point where the water "beads up" and disappears quickly. This is also an opportune time to check for damage due to abrasion from trees, lightning, and wind.

Look for much more on this in Chapter 10.

The Icing on the Cake!

Back on pages 99 -100 we made a few comments on the reasons for using ladder line, which included loss and cost, compared to hard line. Here, with many thanks to Wes Stewart, N7WS is his beautiful loss chart (page 109) that should remove all doubt!

Wes made an exhaustive study of this type of ladder line's loss characteristics, and reported his findings in several papers for the ARRL. The graphic representation's data is based on clean, dry, window type line as described in this article.

Tip: Don't waste short pieces of ladder line — splice, weather seal and use 'em!

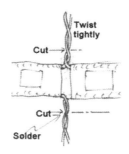

180 degree twist in two feet

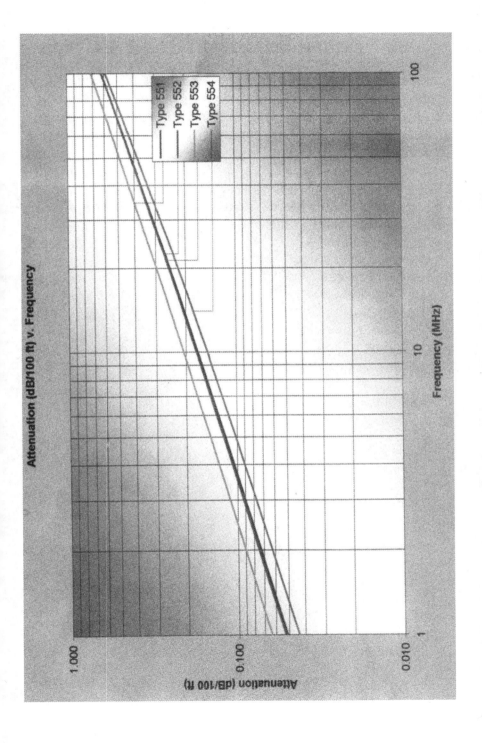

Attenuation (dB/100 ft) v. Frequency

Attenuation (dB/100 ft)

Frequency (MHz)

Type 551
Type 552
Type 553
Type 554

- 115 -

Balanced Line Lightning Precautions

There are a number of steps one can take for this purpose, from the antenna to the radio shack. They differ from coaxial cable, as you might expect, since one of the two conductors cannot be grounded without destroying the balanced condition. Further, balanced line needs to be in a world of its own, wherever it goes, away from anything conductive, reflective, inductive or living that might disturb or distort its "figure 8" RF pattern. Suggestions for accomplishing this are offered in the previous section of this chapter, but lightning protection requires a little different focus.

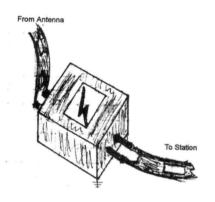

From Antenna

To Station

There is not much one can do at the feed point or on the vertical down route from it unless the feed point is on a tower or pole. At the first change of direction on the way down, an arrestor can provide a first line of defense as well as a means for a 90-degree turn.

Without an arrestor at this point, a wide (1 foot OD) 90-degree sweep gives some protection, since lightning doesn't like to change direction.

If the line approaches ground level further along the path to or just outside of the shack, a ground rod mounted arrestor is excellent protection[1].

On the outside wall, windowsill, or eave of the shack, a double pole, double throw (DPDT) knife

---

[1] p/n CQ880

switch[2] will isolate the station and ground the antenna when not in use. Connect the ladder line to the two center poles of the switch, one pair on one end to the continuing line to the station, and the other pair shorted and connected to the outside station ground. If an entrance panel is used that has feed thru's for ladder line, the DPDT switch may be mounted on the inside for greater convenience.

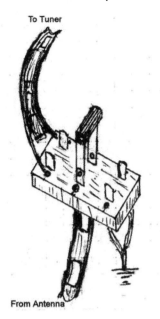

To Tuner

From Antenna

Inside the shack, if balanced line is run directly to the tuner, a good commercial arrestor/suppressor[3] can be used in-line, at the entrance, or right at the tuner.

Any or all of these means of protection should be considered, dependent on the relative risk at your QTH. Assay that risk as suggested in Chapter 5.

A Report from the Country!

We received a letter that described a loop antenna, ladder line fed system that was vaporized by a lightning induced current, all the way to a narrow feed-through terminal where an arc completed the circuit. This is not a new story, since we've received a number of similar tales where the end of the destruction was at an arc, an arrestor or a knife switch (last two illustrations above). They were lucky! Looking back, there is a clear message here:

1.   No antenna (especially wire) should connect to anything within a station without serious lightning protection outside.
2.   The ideal equipment protection inside is complete isolation if at all possible, including the connection to station ground, during electrical storms.

---

[2] p/n 845
[3] I.C.E. 309, for example

3. Never rely on just one device or protocol. Consider the whole QTH, its contents and its inhabitants! Copper and steel vapor in a strike is 4 to 5000 degrees F, and even itty-bitty arcs wipe out solid-state components!

Last stop on the way to the shack is often a lightning arrestor, or even a second one in very high risk areas. This would be, for example, at the bottom of a tower and near the ground just before entrance to the shack. There are several available for balanced line, installable on ground rods, entrance panels, tower bases, etc. Manual disconnects and switches are also utilized as an added precaution or seasonal shutdown protocol.

For extra high lightning-risk areas contact The Wireman for a copy of W4JTL's excellent World Radio article on the subject.

Here's KC7RK's slick windowbox installation! We put it together for him back in '06. His station is hardly visible to his neighbors way up in Seattle – look for him on the air!

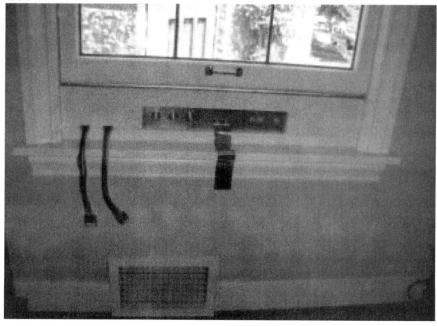

New Ham Commandment VII

Thou shalt not lie......*Giving a fellow operator a 5/9 report for a lousy signal will never help him improve his station and technique. Cheating with power while declaring yourself a QRP station or declaring yourself "mobile" to gain priority in a net are examples of lies that cheapen the hobby for all.*

Antenna Wire

All of the beams and verticals notwithstanding, wire antennas continue to be the most popular device for sending and receiving our amateur radio signals. Probably the main reason is cost, since amateurs are known to be thrifty, but ease of application works for everyone. Dipole theory, as it relates to a bit of wire and lead-in, is one of our earliest bits of exposure to the hobby, and there is no way that we can touch the other side of the world with as much simplicity than by throwing a bit of wire up into a tree.

Happily, another big factor in wire antennas is understanding. Fool around with wire antennas for a while and it's hard not to get a good dose of radio theory that will help enhance the pleasure of the hobby in total. So what's the best kind of wire to use in all of these antennas? Actually, you can't think of one that won't work, but the basics of radio theory lay out some ground rules.

The ideal antenna element is one that is an excellent RF conductor with low surface resistance, uniform construction (ideally, a solid, smooth surface) of a size that is optimum for bandwidth considerations. In a wire antenna it should be of high strength to avoid breakage due to climatic and physical conditions, as well as being able to resist elongation that would affect electrical characteristics. The surface deterioration should be minimal for long life and consistent performance.

Copper-clad Steel, solid

Hard drawn, high strength copper-clad steel of 30% or 40% composite conductivity best satisfies the above criteria, with hard drawn copper a very distant second.

Copper-clad steel (CCS) is a generic expression for the popular trade name, **Copperweld®**[1], and others. It describes an engineered product made by drawing a sandwich of copper wrapped around a core of steel through a die at the right temperature, speed, and tension to result in a fused

---

[1] Trademark of Copperweld Bimetallics, LLC.

product with a core of steel and outer layer of copper, yielding a composite conductivity from 21 to 70% in ASTM defined standards. The temper or hardness of the finished item is based on the end use. It can be as soft as magnet wire or as hard as piano wire, with related elongation factor and break strength.[2]

So what is Antenna CCS?

First, what do we mean by 30 and/or 40% *composite conductivity*? It is not difficult to understand if one takes it step by step, using the conductivity of the two components – copper and steel. Steel, for example, as used in CCS, has a conductivity of a bit less than 9% and the copper has a conductivity of a bit less than 98+%, typical of most industrial copper wire. The actual weight of copper in 40% Composite Conductivity CCS is about 39% and the weight of steel is about 61% of the total. Thus, the weight of of copper times it's conductivity plus the weight of steel times it's conductivity is added to that of copper, making a composite of metals in the conductor totaling 42-43% on the metal conductivity scale, hence 40% plus rating for this CCS..

This doesn't sound too impressive when compared to all copper, but we must now consider the use of this wire for antennas in the HF bands. The actual thickness of the copper layer on the CCS is 12-14% of the radius of 30% composite conductivity and 17-20% of the radius of 40% composite conductivity CCS. The most popular antenna wire in Amateur Radio is the solid 18, 16, and 14 AWG CCS and the radiation performance of all three is equal to that of the same size of hard drawn copper for all of the HF bands, and the strength and the life span is at least double. In stranded models,"Skin effect" of CCS begins to decrease performance of very small strands at 160 meters, so, if you are a "perfectionist," stick to the solid models at 160 meters, but if you miss this information, you probably will never notice the difference!

---

[2] Reference to CCS as described in this text denotes material made to <u>antenna</u> wire specifications.

The occasional complaint in the amateur radio community about copper clad steel is nearly always based on incorrect project design and usage. This is not a surplus product whose specifications are unknown. Antenna CCS wire is designed for antennas. It's as simple as that.

The minimum amount of composite conductivity in top quality antenna CCS is 30% or 40%. 30% is used in the solid or single strand models, and the 40% is used in custom-made stranded types such as the unique "silky" material. These levels serve to provide RF performance on a par with all-copper wire at all HF frequencies, up to 26 AWG "stealth" types..

Tip:

Often, we hear complaints about CCS tangles, kinks, spring-like behavior, and handling difficulty. The tangles are usually the result of using CCS not made and spooled for antennas, so the source is critical. **Antenna CCS wire** as described here is spooled on at least 19 inch OD reels when manufactured, so when re-spooled for orders and use, the main problem is keeping it from unwinding by it-self — just the opposite of messy tangles. Application difficulty is somewhat greater because of the stiffness, but once done, it won't require re-doing for as long as you want it to be up there!

We've also been told and have read stories about sea-coast antennas of CCS dying in less than a year due to salt air, but they all turn out to be wire that was not "Antenna CCS." Consider this: telephone and telegraph wire all over the world was nearly all 30 or 40% CCS nearly a hundred years ago and is now obsolete, but many thrifty Hams salvaged it and it is still "good as gold" as antennas, guy wire, and much more, It is what we now define as "Antenna CCS."

The expression, "good as gold " presents another interesting thought in antenna wire. Plain old conductivity as a
conveyance of electric power points to Copper(100) as
second only to Silver(106^3), and Iron and Steel(9.5) is
close to lousy, with only [316 type]Stainless Steel(2.5)
being worse. Gold(73.4), Aluminum(65) and Bronze(40-
45), but as long as we have anything with copper on the
outside like the CCS, we've got it made for all of the
Amateur bands and we can chuckle at the guys that think
they need gold plated pins in their PL259's!

Hard-drawn and Soft Copper, solid

Plain bare copper wire always will be a popular choice for
antennas, and will perform equally with CCS as regards RF.
The major difference is physical and its ease or difficulty to
work with. It is more malleable than CCS, making assemblies less of a chore. Being all copper, it will not fail due to
corrosion of an exposed core, although a deep nick would so
weaken the wire that the breakage risk would be the same.
Cost, size for size, is almost always greater than CCS due to
the higher copper content.

Regular annealed copper and hard-drawn copper wires
differ in hardness, both by design and use. In the manufacturing process of drawing a given size of wire through a die,
the wire hardens somewhat, making it stiffer and stronger
than wire of the same size that is annealed and has not been
subject to mechanical stress. The most familiar soft annealed wire we see is enameled copper, commonly called
magnet wire, and other bare or jacketed electrical wire. None
of this wire is designed for high lineal strength or limited
stretching. Hard drawn copper is less flexible and somewhat
stronger, making it more desirable for antenna use where
high tension is not likely.

The significant differences between CCS and hard-drawn
copper are breaking strength, elongation and fatigue. CCS
designed for antennas, size for size; has about twice the

---

[3] Data based on Copper as 100%.

breaking strength of hard-drawn copper. CCS has almost no stretch or elongation prior to breaking, whereas hard-drawn copper, although pre-stretched in the drawing and sizing process, will still stretch significantly before reaching its lower breaking point. Finally, CCS is less subject to fatigue damage because of its high strength design. Copper is fatigued by flexing and will fracture when constantly bent or wind-whipped.

Pros and Cons

CCS and all-copper wire will solder equally well, and will last, <u>unstressed</u>, about the same number of years in the same environment, acquiring an equal amount of oxides or other surface deposits, as well as corrosion damage. The hard drawn copper will stretch under its own weight and that of ice or due to wind whip, and therefore its electrical characteristics related to size and length will change. The copper will then break under less than half the load that will cause the CCS to fracture. CCS will not stretch significantly.

Cut or damaged CCS, which has the steel core exposed will rust and self-destruct rapidly if not repaired promptly, but this type of damage is rare due to the way it is used and the high percentage of copper. Solid copper, when cut or damaged in the same manner, will not self destruct, but will fail faster due to weakening. In summary, solid copper is better suited to short antennas such as quads, shorter wavelengths, shorter spans and calmer weather. CCS, designed as antenna wire, is a bit harder to work with, but far and away the best choice for long and more permanent amateur and professional wire antennas. The effort is well worth the occasional band-aid!

Stranded, bare wire

Stranded antenna wire, concentric,[4] in both CCS and hard-drawn copper, is the choice of both commercial and amateur users where greater flexibility and ease of use is paramount or simply preferred. Its RF performance, when new, is equal to that of solid wire, but it degrades faster than solid wire over time. Moisture among the strands becomes

---

[4] "Concentric" is defined in the tables, 7.17-19, for your interest.

the media for corrosion of the individual strands as "acid rain" or other atmospheric contaminants do their thing on the copper or CCS stranded wires, causing noise, weakening, higher RF resistance, and eventually, destruction.

Various construction styles are employed to minimize the degradation and maximize performance, including the number and configuration of strands, type and tightness of "lay," plating, and percentage of copper (for CCS). [5]

Seven strand, 14 AWG[6] copper and CCS are the most common stranded antenna wires, with 12 and 16 AWG used occasionally. 12 gauge is overkill for the great majority of amateur antennas in strength, performance, and cost.

Another development in antenna wire is known as the "Silky" type. It is designed to closely emulate the ideal, solid copper clad steel (30%) in RF propagation, without the disadvantages of stiffness, clock-spring behavior, and actual danger.

The "Silky" type is made up of 19 strands of bare or tinned 40% CCS tightly laid in such a way that all of the individual strands are in total contact with each other. There are minimal air gaps or parallel open conductors. A cross section would show a circle very close to perfect roundness, very close to the cross sectional appearance of solid wire. It is, therefore, very close to solid wire in present and lasting RF performance.

The obvious advantage is the ease of use due to the high flexibility, without sacrifice of performance.[7] One might ask, "If 19 strands are good, wouldn't many more be even better for flexibility?" Theoretically this is true. A more perfect circle cross-section would result. Practically, a 14 AWG wire of

---

[5] "Lay," is the lineal distance required along the side of a stranded wire for any one of the strands to travel 360 degrees.

[6] AWG is American Wire Gauge.

[7] The original "Silky" CCS exhibited a problem in the drawing or sizing of the individual strands, wherein invisible micro-cracks in the copper layer allowed passage of moisture into the steel core, causing rust and early destruction. WM replaced most of this wire after publishing notice of the defect. Subsequent manufacture of bare "Silky" has been with 40% copper, and each strand is tinned, making current production as reliable as 100% copper, albeit with the super strength of CCS.

over 150 strands is possible, but that many strands are very difficult to keep tightly together, and in either pure copper or CCS the inductive loss between strands would be higher. The diode action due to metal salts from trapped moisture and "acid rain" would, in time, make it quite "noisy," and shorter-lived.

Wire of this type of construction is often found in systems designed for dissipative loss such as lightning rod conductor to ground, in electric motors where very flexible, high amperage brush leads, etc. are required, and in welding cables, to name a few. Still, multi-strand high-flex wire used in low stress applications such as quads, short, portable "suitcase," or field-day antenna performs with excellence.[8]

Jacketed stranded wire

The solution to many of the problems with stranded wire is jacketing, many kinds of which are available. The RF behavior of brand new stranded wire and solid wire of the same size and metal is identical within our ability to discern difference. Environment and age make the difference, so, by adding a jacket, the RF characteristics of the stranded wire can be held the same from the time the wire is made until the jacket fails, a difference that is measurable in years.

Very flexible, ultra-violet resistant PVC[9] and polyethylene is available on the several multi-strand copper wires. A tough, high density black polyethylene good for well over 20 years on a group of 19 strand "Silky" CCS makes it useful anywhere from your back yard to the high seas to flying kites and weather balloons (See WM p/n's **531 – 534**).

VF correction for jacketed wire

A reminder: Your pet dipole formula will require a small correction with jacketed wire elements. They will be shorter by 1 to 4 percent due to the lowered velocity factor.

Alternatives

Other varieties of wire for antennas include Alumoweld®[10], an aluminum-clad steel wire. Typical construction

---

[8] See "Flexweave™" by Davis RF, p/n 541-549.

[9] PVC is Polyvinyl Chloride.

[10] Alumoweld is an Alcoa trademark.

calls for 10% aluminum. It would serve well. Aluminum is not far from copper as an RF propagator and it also is more self-protective. The naturally formed aluminum oxide coating will usually seal a cut that opens the steel core to the atmosphere, as opposed to CCS, where the oxidation would proceed unchecked. Unfortunately, the smallest readily available single strand Alumoweld® is 12 AWG, and, it is a bear to work with, more costly, and not at all popular in the amateur community.

Probably the favorite of our older generation of amateurs was *phosphor bronze*. This alloy was the staple of wire antennas for the military for years, and bits of it still turn up from military surplus, estate sales and the like, every so often. This wire is highly corrosion resistant, very strong, and, unfortunately, very expensive. It is not likely that much of it will become available in our market due to cost. Offerings in the amateur community at prices only slightly higher than copper over the past 5 years were not worth repeating, probably because we hams know that it is really not as good a propagator as any CCS or plain copper, and no stronger than CCS.

Textile/wire combinations derived from military applications are becoming more interesting, and could well become an item in the hobby as a combination hi-flex, hi-strength product for portable antennas. See The Wireman new
p/n 512 "HOT ROPE",
Any wire of any type is fair game for an amateur radio antenna in a pinch, from the clothesline to the barbed-wire fence. Some will work well, others poorly, but to miss a chance to get on the air, at least temporarily, is a sin indeed!
A few to avoid!
Farm supply houses sell electric fence wire of various constructions in ¼ mile reels, one of which looks like CCS. This is usually a copper "wash" or very thin plating to avoid rust in storage and help it last for one season of use before discarding - bad news for anything more than a field day or DXpedition dipole! Steel wire for "Mig" welders is also made this way, and also makes a very short-lived antenna wire. Also seen in the market now and then is CCS designed for

coax center conductor use. The typical percentage of copper is 19-21% and the hardness is well below antenna grade. Obviously, such wire is not made for exposure to the elements and, if so used, is doomed to early failure. Performance at 80 and 160 meters is markedly impaired due to the copper thickness in copper-clad steel being less than that required for performance equal to that of solid copper. Current research would seem to indicate that wires of a gauge greater than AWG 26, and 40% copper clad steel wires of a gauge greater than AWG 24 should be avoided for *very* long wire antennas, such as those for 160 meters. The best and most economical solution always boils down to solid CCS of no less than 30% copper at any gauge that is readily available. Stranded wire has it's place but not as CCS smaller than 20 gauge and 40% copper for a beverage at 1.8 MHz if you are a contester!

Additional detailed wire information may be found in the several tables at the end of this section.

Antenna Wire Tips

1. When using any wire for antennas, it should be unwound from its hank or reel in the manner was put into/on the hank or reel. This calls for a human helper doing the "hand over hand" thing in the case of a hank, or a stand and a piece of pipe for a reel. Done in this manner with wire designed for antennas, kinking should never be a problem, since the wire actually has a memory that makes it tend to lie straight. The reverse procedure, when packing up a field day antenna, is just as important. Laying one loop against another with a little thumb and fore-finger twist is a technique that saves a lot of grief on the next outing! Coiling up wire over hand and elbow like rope is like begging for a mess.

This tip is most important for solid wire, but we encourage its use with stranded wire as well, including the rope-like multi-strand material, bare or jacketed. Obviously, kinking is to be avoided for maintaining the strength of the wire and making re-use less of a chore, but the RF performance of stranded wire can be compromised as well. Kinking opens up and separates the strands, changing the "electrical length."

2. Antenna wire breakage is seldom caused by tension in a properly designed wire antenna, since the tension in good design usually will be somewhere between one-sixth to one-tenth of the break strength. Most breakage takes place at junctions where soldering is involved and there is an interface between very stiff soldered wire and flexible virgin wire, where there is an annealed spot that bends easily in the wind. This area can be protected with a one or two-inch "splint" of shrink tube with melt-type lining to minimize bending.

3. There are various ways to attach antenna wire to an insulator, many of which involve stainless steel "eyes." When wire loops under tension rub against metal, wear takes place, not to mention "noise," and damage on any wire can lead to failure. A simple solution is a stainless steel "thimble" in the loop, a "forever" solution (See p/n **800**).

4. Splicing antenna wire? No problem if you do it right with a "Western Union" splice, just like the pioneers used on the telephone and electric wires all over the country. Just twist tightly (tighter than the image) and solder. See Tip 2., above.

5. When cutting multi-strand CCS, tin a spot and then cut through the solder-tinned area. Then check the tinned end of the wire before working with it. This keeps the

**tightly laid strands all together and saves lots of frustra-
tion with the high strength, high temper, really great, CCS
antenna wire!**

Check out the several tables ahead, and see Chapter 8
and its Table of Contents for more information you may
need. There are data of all kinds to help you make a good
choice in the type, size, and support of wire for antennas.

Standard annealed solid copper wire

American Wire Gage AWG	Outside Diameter mils(in/1,000) OD	Cross section Square Inches sq in	Resistance in 1000 ft ohms/1,000ft ohms	Length for R=1 ohm feet	Weight of 1000ft pounds	Length for 1 pound feet
0000	460.0	0.16620	0.04901	20400	640.5	1.561
000	409.6	0.13180	0.06182	16180	507.8	1.969
00	364.8	0.10450	0.07793	12830	402.8	2.482
0	324.9	0.08291	0.09825	10180	319.5	3.130
1	289.3	0.06573	0.12390	8070	253.3	3.947
2	257.6	0.05212	0.15630	6308	200.9	4.978
3	229.4	0.04133	0.19710	5074	159.3	6.278
4	204.3	0.03278	0.24850	4024	126.3	7.915
5	181.0	0.02599	0.31340	3100	100.2	9.984
6	162.0	0.02061	0.39520	2530	79.44	12.59
7	144.3	0.01635	0.49810	2008	63.03	15.87
8	128.5	0.01297	0.62810	1892	49.98	20.01
9	114.4	0.01028	0.73250	1262	39.62	25.24
10	101.9	0.00816	0.99880	1001	31.43	31.82
11	90.7	0.00646	1.26	793	24.90	40.20
12	80.8	0.00513	1.59	629	19.80	50.60
13	72.0	0.00407	2.00	500	15.70	63.70
14	64.1	0.00323	2.52	396	12.40	80.40
15	57.1	0.00256	3.18	314	9.87	101
16	50.8	0.00203	4.02	249	7.81	128
17	45.3	0.00161	5.05	198	6.21	161
18	40.3	0.00128	6.39	157	4.92	203
19	35.9	0.00101	8.05	124	3.90	256
20	32.0	0.000804	10.1	98.7	3.10	323
21	23.5	0.000638	12.8	78.3	2.46	407
22	25.3	0.000503	16.2	61.7	1.94	516
23	22.6	0.000401	20.3	40.2	1.55	647
24	20.1	0.000317	25.7	39.0	1.22	818
25	17.9	0.000252	32.4	30.9	0.97	1,030
26	15.9	0.000199	41.0	24.4	0.765	1,310
27	14.2	0.000158	51.4	19.4	0.610	1,640
28	12.6	0.000125	65.3	15.3	0.481	2,080
29	11.3	0.000100	81.2	12.3	0.387	2,590
30	10.0	0.0000785	104.0	9.64	0.303	3,300

Resistivity of hard drawn copper is about 2.5% higher.
(NBS-HB-100)

Standard annealed solid copper wire

American Wire Gage	Outside Diameter	Cross section Square	Resistance in 1000 ft	Length for	Weight of	Length for
	mils(in/1,000)	inches	ohms/1,000ft	R=1 ohm	1000ft	1 pound
AWG	OD	sq in	ohms	feet	pounds	feet
31	8.9	0.0000622	131.0	7.64	0.240	4,170
32	8.0	0.0000503	162.0	6.17	0.104	5,160
33	7.1	0.0000396	205.0	4.86	0.153	6,550
34	6.3	0.0000312	261.0	3.83	0.120	8,320
35	5.6	0.0000246	331.0	3.02	0.0949	10,500
36	5.0	0.0000106	415.0	2.41	0.0757	13,200
37	4.5	0.0000159	512.0	1.95	0.0613	16,300
38	4.0	0.0000120	648.0	1.54	0.0484	20,600
39	3.5	0.00000962	847.0	1.18	0.0371	27,000
40	3.1	0.00000755	1080.0	0.927	0.0291	34,400
41	2.8	0.00000916	1320.0	0.756	0.0237	42,100
42	2.5	0.00000491	1060.0	0.603	0.0189	52,900
43	2.2	0.00000380	2140.0	0.467	0.0147	68,300
44	2.0	0.00000314	2590.0	0.386	0.0121	82,600
45	1.76	0.00000243	3350.0	0.299	0.03938	107,000
46	1.57	0.00000194	4210.0	0.238	0.00746	134,000
47	1.40	0.00000154	5290.0	0.189	0.00593	169,000
48	1.24	0.00000121	6750.0	0.148	0.00465	215,000
49	1.11	0.000000968	8420.0	0.119	0.00373	268,000
50	0.99	0.000000770	10600.0	0.0945	0.00297	337,000
51	0.33	0.000000608	13400.0	0.0747	0.00234	427,000
52	0.78	0.000000478	17000.0	0.0587	0.00184	543,000
53	0.70	0.000000385	21200.0	0.0472	0.00148	674,000
54	0.62	0.000000302	27000.0	0.0371	0.00116	859,000
55	0.55	0.000000238	34300.0	0.0292	0.000916	1,090,000
56	0.49	0.000000189	43200.0	0.0232	0.000727	1,380,000

Resistivity of hard drawn copper is about 2.5% higher.
(NBS-HB-100)

SOLID 30% COPPER-CLAD STEEL PROPERTIES					
Amer. Wire Gauge AWG	Diameter Inches	Weight Per 1000 ft Pounds	Nominal DC Resistance Per 1000 ft Ohms	Break Strength Pounds	Conser-vative Tension Pounds
0	0.3249	292.49	0.328	–	–
1	0.2893	231.91	0.413	–	–
2	0.2576	183.87	0.521	6412	641
3	0.2284	145.82	0.657	5519	552
4	0.2043	115.65	0.828	4672	467
5	0.1819	91.68	1.045	3913	391
6	0.1620	72.72	1.317	3247	325
7	0.1443	57.70	1.660	2681	268
8	0.1285	45.75	2.094	2204	220
9	0.1144	36.26	2.642	1790	179
10	0.1019	28.77	3.329	1460	146
11	0.0907	22.79	4.203	1153	115
12	0.0808	18.09	5.295	917	92
13	0.0720	14.36	6.669	720	72
14	0.0641	11.39	8.414	550	55
15	0.0571	9.03	10.604	473	47
16	0.0508	7.15	13.397	381	38
17	0.0453	5.69	16.847	306	31
18	0.0403	4.50	21.287	280	28
19	0.0359	3.57	26.825	222	22
20	0.0320	2.84	33.761	176	18
21	0.0285	2.25	42.563	140	14
22	0.0253	1.77	54.011	110	11
23	0.0226	1.42	67.687	88	9
24	0.0201	1.12	85.571	69	7

Shaded items are the most commonly used for amateur antennas. 30% CCS is sufficient for all HF wire antennas.

SOLID 40% COPPER-CLAD STEEL PROPERTIES					
Amer. Wire Gauge AWG	Diameter Inches	Weight Per 1000 ft Pounds	Nominal DC Resistance Per 1000 ft Ohms	Break Strength Pounds	Conservative Tension Pounds
0	0.3249	295.48	0.246	–	–
1	0.2893	234.27	0.310	–	–
2	0.2576	181.75	0.391	5450	545
3	0.2284	147.30	0.493	4691	469
4	0.2043	116.93	0.621	3971	397
5	0.1819	92.62	0.784	3326	333
6	0.1620	73.46	0.988	2759	276
7	0.1443	58.29	1.245	2278	228
8	0.1285	46.22	1.570	1873	187
9	0.1144	36.63	1.981	1521	152
10	0.1019	29.07	2.497	1241	124
11	0.0907	23.03	3.152	980	98
12	0.0808	18.27	3.972	779	78
13	0.0720	14.51	5.002	612	61
14	0.0641	11.50	6.311	503	50
15	0.0571	9.13	7.953	402	40
16	0.0508	7.22	10.047	323	32
17	0.0453	5.74	12.635	260	26
18	0.0403	4.55	15.965	238	24
19	0.0359	3.61	20.118	188	19
20	0.0320	2.87	25.321	149	15
21	0.0285	2.27	31.922	118	12
22	0.0253	1.79	40.508	93	9
23	0.0226	1.43	60.765	75	8
24	0.0201	1.13	64.179	59	6

40 % conductivity table is shown for comparison and interest. Not normally stocked.

19 Strand bare CCS
Low Carbon and Hi-Strength (30 & 40%)

Amer. Wire Gauge	Construction No. strands strand size	Nominal Diameter inches	Circular Mils sq	Max DC Resistance Ohms/M ft@68F		Nominal Weight Pounds		Nominal Break Pounds		
				30%	40%	30%	40%	30%HS	40%HS 30%LC	40%LC
7	19/.032	0.1600	19,380	1.92	1.44	55.72	57.12	1,746	1,512	1,306
8	19/.0285	0.1430	15,428	2.43	1.82	44.22	45.32	1,386	1200	1,036
9	19/.0253	0.1270	12,160	3.08	2.32	34.86	25.73	1,092	946	817
10	19/.0226	0.1130	9,709	3.85	2.89	27.79	28.49	871	754	651
11	19/.0201	0.1000	7,676	4.87	3.66	21.97	22.52	688	596	515
12	19/.0179	0.0895	6,080	6.16	4.62	17.47	17.90	547	474	409
13	19/.0159	0.0795	4,807	7.83	5.87	13.79	14.14	432	374	323
14	19/.0142	0.0710	3,838	9.71	7.28	10.95	11.23	343	297	257
15	19/.0126	0.0630	3,020	12.35	9.27	8.66	8.88	272	235	203
16	19/.0113	0.0565	2,432	15.39	11.54	6.93	7.11	217	188	162
17	19/.010	0.0500	1,900	19.69	14.77	5.44	5.58	171	148	128
18	19/.0089	0.0445	1,505	24.92	18.70	4.31	4.42	135	117	101
19	19/.008	0.0400	1,216	30.92	23.20	3.49	3.57	109	95	82
20	19/.0063	0.0315	754	50.21	37.66	2.16	2.22	68	59	51
24	19/.005	0.0250	475	80.38	60.30	1.36	1.39	43	37	32
26	19/.004	0.0200	304	123.08	92.32	0.87	0.89	27	24	20

19 Strand tinned CCS
Low Carbon and Hi-Strength (30 & 40%)

Amer. Wire Gauge	Construction No. strands strand size	Nominal Diameter inches	Circular Mils mils sq	Max DC Resistance Ohms/M ft@68F 30%	40%	Nominal Weight Pounds 30%	40%	Nominal Break Pounds 30%HS	40%HS	40%LC
7	19/.032	0.1600	19,380	2.21	1.60	55.72	57.12	1,746	1,512	1,306
8	19/.0285	0.1430	15,428	2.79	2.02	44.22	45.32	1,386	1200	1,036
9	19/.0253	0.1270	12,160	3.55	2.57	34.86	25.73	1,092	946	817
10	19/.0226	0.1130	9,709	4.42	3.20	27.79	28.49	871	754	651
11	19/.0201	0.1000	7,676	5.61	4.05	21.97	22.52	688	596	515
12	19/.0179	0.0895	6,080	7.69	5.42	17.47	17.90	547	474	409
13	19/.0159	0.0795	4,807	9.77	6.90	13.79	14.14	432	374	323
14	19/.0142	0.0710	3,838	12.11	8.55	10.95	11.23	343	297	257
15	19/.0126	0.0630	3,020	15.41	10.88	8.66	8.88	272	235	203
16	19/.0113	0.0565	2,432	19.20	13.55	693	7.11	217	188	162
17	19/.010	0.0500	1,900	25.67	17.90	5.44	5.58	171	148	128
18	19/.0089	0.0445	1,505	32.49	22.65	4.31	4.42	135	117	101
19	19/.008	0.0400	1,216	40.32	28.11	3.49	3.57	109	95	82
20	19/.0063	0.0315	754	65.46	45.64	2.16	2.22	68	59	51
24	19/.005	0.0250	475	104.80	73.07	1.36	1.39	43	37	32
26	19/.004	0.0200	304	160.46	111.87	0.87	0.89	27	24	20

7 Strand, Copper clad steel

AWG	Construction #/In	Circular Mils	Nom. Diam. inches	Max DC Res Ohms/M ft 30%	40%	Nom. Weight lbs/M ft 30%	40%	Nom. Break Lbs 30% HS	40%HS / 30%LC	40%LC
11	7/.032	7,140	0.0960	5.11	3.84	20.14	20.43	643	557	481
12	7/.0314	6,252	0.0892	6.12	4.48	16.49	17.30	584	506	437
13	7/.0283	5,366	0.0825	7.16	5.22	13.27	13.56	478	416	351
14	7/.0253	4,480	0.0759	8.22	6.17	12.60	12.78	403	349	301
15	7/.0226	3,577	0.0678	10.24	7.68	10.04	10.29	321	278	240
16	7/.0201	2,828	0.0603	12.97	9.73	7.94	8.14	254	220	190
17	7/.0179	2,240	0.0537	16.40	12.30	6.31	6.47	202	175	151
18	7/.0159	1,771	0.0477	20.84	15.64	4.98	5.11	159	138	119
19	7/.0142	1,414	0.0426	25.84	19.39	3.96	4.06	126	110	95
20	7/.0126	1,113	0.0378	32.88	24.67	3.13	3.21	100	87	75
21	7/.0113	896	0.0337	40.96	30.72	2.50	2.57	80	69	60
22	7/.010	700	0.0300	52.42	39.32	1.97	2.01	63	54	47
23	7/.0089	554	0.0267	66.35	49.77	1.56	1.60	50	43	37
24	7/.008	448	0.0240	82.32	61.76	1.26	1.29	40	35	30
25	7/.0071	353	0.0213	104.85	78.66	0.99	1.02	32	27	24
26	7/.0063	278	0.0189	133.66	100.26	0.78	0.80	25	22	19
27	7/.0056	220	0.0168	169.85	127.41	0.62	0.63	20	17	15
28	7/.005	175	0.0150	214.00	160.52	0.49	0.50	16	14	12
29	7/.0045	140	0.0135	258.29	193.76	0.40	0.41	13	11	10
30	7/.004	112	0.0120	327.64	245.77	0.31	0.32	10	9	8
31	7/.0035	84	0.0105	426.70	320.09	0.24	0.25	8	7	6
32	7/.0031	70	0.0093	545.14	408.93	0.18	0.19	6	5	5

Concentric Strand Wire[11]

Stranded conductors were developed as a means of overcoming the rigidity of solid wires while retaining electrical conductivity. For any given overall wire size, building the cable with a greater number of strands (and corresponding decrease in individual member wire size) will result in an improvement in flexibility. Note that insulated wire flexibility is further affected by the type and thickness of insulation.

True concentric strand is composed of a central wire surrounded by one or more layers of helically laid wires, with the direction of lay reversed for successive layers and with the length of lay increased for each successive layer. Unless otherwise specified, the direction of lay of the outer layer is left-hand. Concentric stranding has greater mechanical strength and better crush resistance over other types of stranding. Of all constructions, concentric's almost circular cross section permits best centering of the conductor within the insulation.

The stranded constructions can be manufactured in annealed, medium hard, and hard states. They can be manufactured bare or tinned. The length of lay for each construction is determined by customer requirements according to the need of smoothness and the flexibility in each application.

New Ham Commandment VIII

Thou shalt keep the frequency holy......*Check to see that the frequency is clear before making a call, move away when politely asked, and don't knowingly interfere with the transmissions of others. Remember that it is "first come, first served" and **nobody** "owns" a frequency.*

---

[11] This discussion is provided for the reader's interest related to the development of the "Silky" type antenna wire. The text is from the old *Laribee Wire Manufacturing Company*'s technical literature, which was heavily relied upon in the creation of these products for the amateur radio community. Laribee is no longer around, but their fine products and technology live on.

Concentric 7-Strand Copper Cable

Size AWG	Circular Mil. Area	Number of Wires	Diameter of Strand (inches)	Approx. Dia. Cable (inches)	Approx. Wt. per 1000 ft. (lbs.)
1	83,690	7	.1093	.332	258
2	66,360	7	.0974	.292	205
3	52,620	7	.0867	.260	163
4	41,740	7	.0772	.232	129
6	26,240	7	.0612	.184	81
8	16,510	7	.0486	.146	51
10	10,380	7	.0385	.115	32
12	6,530	7	.0305	.091	20
14	4,110	7	.0242	.073	13
16	2,580	7	.0192	.058	8
18	1,620	7	.0152	.046	5
20	1,020	7	.0121	.036	3
22	704	7	.010	.030	2
24	448	7	.008	.024	1.35
26	278	7	.0063	.019	.85
28	175	7	.005	.015	.54
30	110	7	.004	.012	.34
32	63	7	.003	.009	.21

Concentric 19-Strand Copper Cable

Size AWG	Circular Mil. Area	Number of Wires	Diameter of Strand (inches)	Approx. Dia. Cable (inches)	Approx. Wt. per 1000 ft. (lbs.)
4/0	211,600	19	.1055	.528	653
3/0	167,800	19	.0940	.470	518
2/0	133,100	19	.0837	.419	411
1/0	105,600	19	.0745	.372	326
1	83,690	19	.0664	.332	258
2	66,380	19	.0591	.296	205
4	41,740	19	.0469	.235	129
6	26,240	19	.0372	.186	81
8	16,510	19	.0295	.148	51
10	10,380	19	.0234	.117	32
12	6,530	19	.0185	.093	20
14	4,110	19	.0147	.074	12.7
16	2,580	19	.0117	.059	8
18	1,620	19	.0092	.046	5
20	1,020	19	.0073	.037	3
22	704	19	.0063	.032	2.4
24	448	19	.0050	.025	1.5

New Ham Commandment IX

Honor thy father and mother……And anyone else at or near your QTH. Maintain a clean signal that does not interfere with their stereo, TV, or other electronics. If you have a problem and cannot fix it, work out a compromise such as "quiet hours" or lower power until you can. Don't let your problem or lack of skill become a problem for someone else.

New Ham Commandment X

Thou shalt keep a clean mouth……It has been said that profanity is the feeble attempt of a small mind to express it-self. Freedom of speech does not justify offending the sensi-bilities of others.

The Ubiquitous Dipole or Loop

Physically they are not quite the same, but for our purpose here, they are dealt with equally. We could cite the "*Folded Dipole*" for nit-pickers!

These wire antennas are such an integral part of amateur radio that there will always be more to be discussed, written and forgotten on the subject. We will not define an antenna for any specific size or frequency, but we hope to help you assemble one that will perform as well or better than many of the kits or ready-to-use units on the market.

They're everywhere!

They're all the same and they're all different, but for the most of us they are the easiest and most effective way to enjoy our hobby on the HF bands. We've preached for years that a simple "Flat Top" of almost any length up at almost any height, center fed with any kind of ladderline from almost any balanced feed station setup with a good tuner, will produce more bang (and fun) for the buck than any discrete antenna in the book(s).

We won't go into the details of a particular antenna, but will try to make it easier to put one together and KEEP it up for as long as you please.

First, decide how the antenna will be used. Will it be at your QTH, "permanent," temporary, "invisible," or perhaps packed in your suitcase or knapsack for vacation trips, field day, etc.?

We invite you to peruse Chapter 10 here in WIREBOOK V, where we've included a few of the many wire antennas we've helped with to some extent. These guys have done a great job and we're proud to help tell their stories!

"Wire" we here?

The heart of the antenna is the wire, and the correct wire depends on the use. For example, the best permanent wire antenna uses bare, solid, high strength 30% or 40% composite conductivity copper clad steel (CCS), *DESIGNED FOR ANTENNAS,* and of a size appropriate to the unsupported length and the location[1]. It will perform the same in 1, 10, 20, 30 or more years, if installed and maintained properly. Many amateurs dislike CCS because it can be springy and hard to work with, but if one considers its longevity, performance, and price, there is simply no contest, and using it is well worth the effort.

Portability is sometimes a must; so stranded CCS wire is also very popular. It is easier to work with in every respect, and, it will, *WHEN NEW*, perform just as well as solid wire. On the down side, it can be somewhat more expensive at the outset, and, if bare, it will have a shorter lifespan, depending on the environment. Moisture gets between the strands and eats away the copper at a rate dependant on the pH and make-up of the precipitation in their area ("acid rain," salt air, etc.). This destructive action also makes reception noisier with aging, due to the thousands of tiny semiconductors born of this process.

Solid, stranded, and multi-stranded copper and copper alloys are also popular antenna choices, especially for their ease of use. Various commercial and consumer copper wires, readily available from amateur radio suppliers and hardware stores, are used, as well as rope-like multistranded wire which is extremely flexible[2]. Reference is often made to "*hard drawn*" copper wire for antennas for it's higher break strength, but, size for size, the all-copper wires have no better than half the breaking strength of CCS, thus limiting the unsupported span length and can require resizing due to stretching. The RF characteristics of all-copper antenna wire are the same as those of CCS in our HF bands, as are the prices. The bare wire etching/corrosion problems are the same as those described for stranded CCS.

Last, but not least, are the growing number of *stranded and jacketed* CCS and all-copper antenna wires. All of the conveniences of the different levels of flexibility are enjoyed. All ranges of strength and ruggedness are available in different colors and even "invisible" wire, tiny and strong, for

---

[1] "Copperweld®"is a trademark of *Copperweld Bimetallics LLC,* the well-known manufacturer of CCS.

[2] Davis RF "Flexweave"®

"stealth" antennas. Climatic conditions don't shorten jacketed wire's lifespan if the terminations are well sealed, making at lifespan similar to that of solid wire. Surprise: The price is just a bit higher than bare wire!

Summing up, you can't go wrong because they all work! The differences are only in the tailoring when covering your needs with the wire that best fits your situation. Please see the Antenna Wire section in the catalog for a complete description of the many types, designed for any way you choose to fly!

Are you ready?

We really don't have to wait til winter to put up our dipole, no matter what amateur radio tradition dictates, so let's have at it!

You should study the site carefully and then put up the biggest, most versatile, longest lasting, broad-banded, and cost-effective antenna that will fit into your pocket book and the space available. This could turn out to be anything from a 16 foot, 10 meter wonder between the house and garage, to a multi-hundred foot whopper between the house, poles, trees, barn, garage, and privy!

(fig.1) Note that the sketches can be either a side or top view.

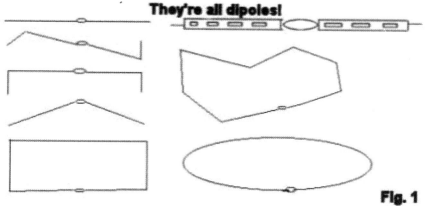

Fig. 1

The ideal simple "all HF band antenna," can be most any length of wire fed with ladderline and matched to the transmitter through a decent tuner or matchbox. A conjugate match is attained at most any HF frequency **if** enough radiating surface is provided. Enhancements such as other wild patterns dictated by the trees and poles available, and the use of ladderline as a radiator (fig.1), are just different ways to skin the cat. This is not meant to deter the purist from cutting the perfect wire antenna from the various formulas and recipes, but **that exact length antenna is only "perfect" at one frequency and possibly a harmonic of another by chance or design.** However, with a good tuner and enough wire, you've got it all!

The word "tower" is absent above, since most of us in the real world don't have one, and the essence of our hobby is improvisation. Don't hesitate to use one if it's handy, however! We're really not talking to extreme contesters here, just hams that enjoy the hobby on their own terms.

Now for the fun part. Arm yourself with ladder, rope, hardware, safety gear, and a friend, and have at it! Without a ladder, there's a slingshot, bow and arrow, potato gun, cross bow, and balloon. All are alternates, but we'll let you

choose the toys for your particular playground!

Please refer to fig. 2 (next page) for an overall concept of the job and a variety of options, useful for any wire antenna..

A dipole works best if:
1. The center is even with or higher than the ends.
2. The feed line runs at 90 degrees from the horizontal and vertical planes of the elements (wires) for as long as possible. Do the best you can.

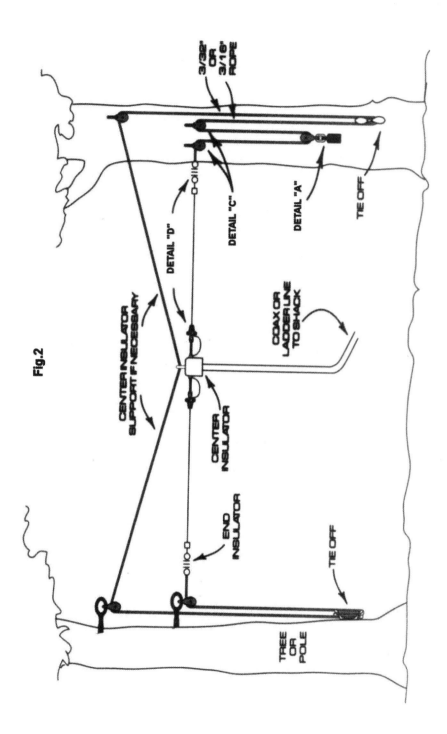

Fig.2

3/32" OR 3/16" ROPE

DETAIL "D"

DETAIL "C"

DETAIL "A"

TIE OFF

CENTER INSULATOR SUPPORT IF NECESSARY

COAX OR LADDER LINE TO SHACK

CENTER INSULATOR

END INSULATOR

TIE OFF

TREE OR POLE

3. The elements run free from any conductive material (foliage, metallic and wet surfaces, and overhead wires-- dead or alive). *Never over live wires!*

The center height is whatever works for you. This is blasphemy to the theorist, and we're not going to go there. The point is doing the best you can without danger to life and limb. The lower the frequency, the higher the dipole, is a very rough rule of thumb, but any height will work well enough to enjoy the hobby, so don't give up if all you have is a fence post and garage roof!

Practically speaking, when trees are utilized for support, you must provide for their random motion due to wind. See fig. 2 and **Detail "A" and "C."** Pulleys, used generously to facilitate erection, repairs, changes, and inspection, will seem pretty cheap in a big wind or on the day of a major winter ice storm!

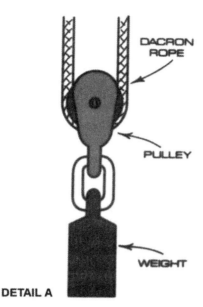

DETAIL A

1. The 3/32" UV resistant polyester (Dacron™) rope is good for almost every form of dipole support. Its nominal breaking strength of 260 lbs is less than that of most copper clad steel antenna wires, which is an additional safety factor in a catastrophe. Heavier rope is available for unusually long spans, and a nomograph is available to calculate stresses, sag and loads (page 163).

2. The use of a compound pulley system (**Detail "A" and "C"**) better maintains the desired tension in the support system. More weight is required, but the travel distance is less, reducing violent movement in a storm.

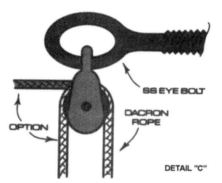

DETAIL "C"

3. Good, reasonably priced pulleys are hard to find. The best we've seen, short of a high-priced marine supply house, have a brass wheel with tight enough clearance in the frame to keep the small rope in the groove, and the body is well plated for marine use. They are rated to 100+ pounds, good for most dipole systems.[3]

4. If it is possible to get up to the hanging points in trees, etc., stainless steel, eye-type lag screws are the best choice for support, and will last a lifetime in trees if backed out a little every 5 years or so to compensate for tree growth.

---

[3] See p/n's **890** and **891**.

5. If the support ropes get up into trees by other means, it pays to lower and check them out yearly for abrasion damage and sticking in bark and growth.

6. The life of all types of wire can be extended immeasurably by the use of stainless steel thimbles[4] at wear points **(Detail "D")**. Continuity is assured by wiring around this point.

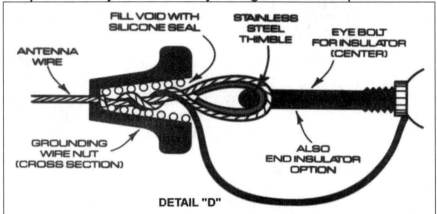

DETAIL "D"

7. Soldering should be done in such a way that the soldered portion and the virgin wire adjacent to it on either side are not subject to continuous flexing after installation. Such areas are most susceptible to breakage.

8. Again consider **Detail "D"** and the **grounding wire nut.** This is a handy way to make a good electrical connection without heat damage due to soldering. It makes adjustment for electrical length easy, and when the job is done, filling the cavity with silicone cement protects the wire and avoids unwinding. (Don't worry about the warnings you hear that this sealant will eat up the copper wire. The vinegary, acetic acid smell disappears on curing along with its etching power, if any, proven with major brands).

Another version of this approach, making the job even simpler, is shown on page 150, next. This is an even simpler way to do the job at all of the wire terminations in dipole construction and adjustment. Used in conjunction with the stainless steel thimbles, all of the stress and abrasion points

---

[4] p/n **800, 800A**

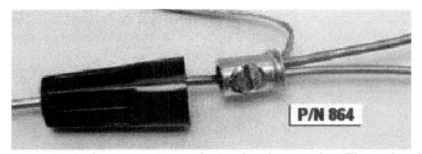

P/N 864

are protected, no matter what wire is used. The wire is passed through the cap and brass slug from left to right, then around a thimble and through the eyebolt and back into the slug along with a piece of tinned copper braid which leads to the terminal on the balun or center insulator. The setscrew is tightened, the cap screwed on, and, when the adjustment re-do's are done, the cap is filled with silicone sealant.

9. If you chose to feed your dipole with coax, tuning is more difficult, but worth it if you are a "one band, one frequency" operator. Resonance is sometimes accompanied by a higher than acceptable SWR, for a wide variety of reasons. If there is a physical 1/4 wave of wire in each leg in this case, a common cause is unequal electrical length. Instead of trimming each side equally, try adding some length with a clip lead to just one side at a time. This method often provides lower SWR at resonance at the desired frequency. The clip lead length can then be added in antenna wire to the test side or removed from the other side. Another reason for an apparent mismatch can be your choice of coax. Check out the next article, **"Coax fed dipole – 50 or 75 ohm?"**

Good luck with your dipole, the sequels are up to you. A good amateur learns something with every project. Send in your ideas and we'll see to it that they are shared! (See Chapter 10)

As for the cat

Just kidding!

Coax fed dipole - 50 or 75 ohm?

This is a pretty common question from both old and new hams, and it's always controversial. Match the antenna or match the feed line.

Since most all of today's equipment is based on 50 ohms, it makes no sense to use 75-ohm coax if you have to purchase it. The very small mismatch should be at the antenna, where you always will have a mismatch at every frequency other than that of perfect resonance. True, a perfect dipole in a perfect setting will have input impedance closer to 75 ohms than to 50 ohms at the design frequency, but it is almost irrelevant, since you'll only operate at that point by chance as you tune across the band. Many of today's solid-state transceivers have built-in "tuners" which will take care of a 1.5:1 SWR at resonance and somewhat beyond in either direction, depending on the band and the range of the components therein. The rig wants to see 50 ohms, so it's logical to feed its output into a 50 ohm feed line, putting the mismatch as far away as possible, minimizing the correction required from the tuner.

A "real," stand alone tuner in the station is always the best way to enjoy much more bandwidth on the band for which the dipole is cut, as well as at harmonics on other bands.

How to remove all of the confusion!

If you really want to have a ball on HF, put up the longest wire antenna that easily fits at your QTH and feed it with any length of ladder line from a decent tuner. Chances are that you'll be able to work almost anywhere you want to, from 1 to at least 30 MHz! If it's a typical dipole, the length of each side will be the length of the feed line, which is part of the load, plus the length of one side of the antenna up there in the air.

For example, a 110 foot dipole fed with 75 feet of ladder-line will present 55+75 X 2 = 260 feet of wire to the tuner terminals, enough to resonate on 160 meters. The tuner could deal with a number of feet more or less than the example, depending on the size of its components.

So what's a good tuner?

The big old Johnson Matchbox from years gone by exemplifies the most significant characteristics: huge coils and capacitors that could supply a huge range of reactance that would match the aggregate impedance presented by an antenna at any given frequency. Today's tuners are of a wide range of capability, and there are many that offer up to 2000 ohms or more[5] – perfect for random lengths of antenna wire and ladderline. Shop carefully, be very aware of this feature. Don't be fooled by transceiver built-in tuners that are just "trimmers," good for fine tuning only. We call them "kinda tuners."

The formula for calculating wire length for an antenna is based on the half wave dipole formula. Some books use the formula, L=492/F and others use L=468/F. The 492 is based on the speed of RF on a radiator or the speed of light in a perfect vacuum. For practical use this must be modified for the presence of air (the atmosphere), insulation or other impediments to RF, and the general surroundings at the site (trees, water, tin roofs, etc.). The proper starting point for building a half-wave, bare-wire dipole for a specific frequency, is L=468/F, which uses a velocity factor of 95% (492X.95). This is typical at sea level and up to a few thousand feet anywhere on earth.

Insulated antenna wire would lower the velocity factor and would thus require a correction (shortening) of some 1 to 3%, depending on the type and thickness of the jacket.

Use of the 492 figure would be, for example, for cutting a half-wave length of coax of a specific VF of, say, 66%, like RG58/U. For 3.8 MHz, 492/3.8 X 0.66= 85.45 feet. Such a length of coax would show data at the transceiver identical to that at the feed point of any load, for design purposes, etc. *at that frequency only.*

L o o o n g Wire Antennas

Many years ago on my farm in Michigan, I got a little "six-pack" help from friends and the power company and sunk a pair of 70-foot poles 500+ feet apart in the north field. I even

---

[5] See especially balanced tuners by Palstar, MFJ, or build one yourself!

remembered to install a pulley on top of each in the middle of 125 feet of rope!

I then proceeded to make every mistake in the book in the art of Long-Wire antenna building, but it was a great learning experience and solid proof of the, "..learn-by-your-mistakes..." theorem.

Finally, with a lot of help from a paper-back "Elmer", titled "*73 Dipole and Long-Wire Antennas*" by Ed Noll, W3FQJ, I began to really enjoy amateur radio with a great dipole and my "Green Machines" from Heathkit.

The fun began with learning that half-wave dipoles can consist of a quarter-wave on one side and any odd number of quarter-waves on the other side. My 40-meter dipole with fifteen quarter waves between the poles, and one QW sloping almost straight down from the near pole, was a "killer."

The next delightful experience was learning that 15 quarter waves on 40 was very close in length to 29 QW's on 20, 43 on 15, and 59 on 10, and that, with only two more single QW's on the short side, I was in business on 4 bands! Further, if it had been last year instead of 30+ years ago, The WARC bands were there with ease!

The last "miracle" in this happy saga of the '70's was ladder line and a good tuner, whereby I could go anywhere I chose to go across the HF bands and seldom, if ever, get even close to a 2:1 SWR!

If you have a "back 40" or even a "California Ranch" (2 acres!), here is an inexpensive way to reach the world with ease and actually compete with a beam's gain in the same direction as the long wire in both long and short path operation, by changing the height of the far end with the pulley system.

We collect many stories from hams that have had similar experience stories after the revelation of the easy and inexpensive random wire antennas fed with random length ladderline from a good tuner with broad range. We will share some of them with you elsewhere in WIREBOOK V. Meanwhile, check out the following chart before your next dipole!

No. of 1/4 waves	VF=.95 Times 234	Feet at frequency								
		28.4	24.96	21.3	18.14	14.2	10.13	7.3	3.9	1.8
1	234	8.2	9.4	11.0	12.9	16.5	23.1	32.0	59.9	129.8
3	701	24.7	28.1	32.9	38.6	49.4	69.2	96.0	179.8	389.5
5	1169	41.1	46.8	54.9	64.4	82.3	115.4	160.1	299.6	649.2
7	1636	57.6	65.5	76.8	90.2	115.2	161.5	224.1	419.5	908.8
9	2103	74.1	84.3	98.7	115.9	148.1	207.6	288.1	539.3	1168.5
11	2571	90.5	103.0	120.7	141.7	181.0	253.8	352.2	659.2	1428.2
13	3038	107.0	121.7	142.6	167.5	214.0	299.9	416.2	779.0	1687.8
15	3506	123.4	140.4	164.6	193.2	246.9	346.1	480.2	898.8	1947.5
17	3973	139.9	159.2	186.5	219.0	279.8	392.2	544.2	1018.7	2207.2
19	4440	156.3	177.9	208.5	244.8	312.7	438.3	608.3	1138.5	2466.8
21	4908	172.8	196.6	230.4	270.5	345.6	484.5	672.3	1258.4	2726.5
23	5375	189.3	215.3	252.4	296.3	378.5	530.6	736.3	1378.2	2986.2
25	5843	205.7	234.1	274.3	322.1	411.4	576.8	800.3	1498.1	3245.8
27	6310	222.2	252.8	296.2	347.8	444.4	622.9	864.4	1617.9	3505.5
29	6777	238.6	271.5	318.2	373.6	477.3	669.0	928.4	1737.8	3765.2
31	7245	255.1	290.3	340.1	399.4	510.2	715.2	992.4	1857.6	4024.8
33	7712	271.6	309.0	362.1	425.1	543.1	761.3	1056.5	1977.5	4284.5
35	8180	288.0	327.7	384.0	450.9	576.0	807.5	1120.5	2097.3	4544.2
37	8647	304.5	346.4	406.0	476.7	608.9	853.6	1184.5	2217.2	4803.8
39	9114	320.9	365.2	427.9	502.4	641.9	899.7	1248.5	2337.0	5063.5
41	9582	337.4	383.9	449.8	528.2	674.8	945.9	1312.6	2456.8	5323.2
43	10049	353.8	402.6	471.8	554.0	707.7	992.0	1376.6	2576.7	5582.8
45	10517	370.3	421.3	493.7	579.7	740.6	1038.2	1440.6	2696.5	5842.5
47	10984	386.8	440.1	515.7	605.5	773.5	1084.3	1504.6	2816.4	6102.2
49	11451	403.2	458.8	537.6	631.3	806.4	1130.4	1568.7	2936.2	6361.8
51	11919	419.7	477.5	559.6	657.0	839.3	1176.6	1632.7	3056.1	6621.5
53	12386	436.1	496.2	581.5	682.8	872.3	1222.7	1696.7	3175.9	6881.2
55	12854	452.6	515.0	603.5	708.6	905.2	1268.9	1760.8	3295.8	7140.8
57	13321	469.0	533.7	625.4	734.3	938.1	1315.0	1824.8	3415.6	7400.5
59	13788	485.5	552.4	647.3	760.1	971.0	1361.1	1888.8	3535.5	7660.2
61	14256	502.0	571.1	669.3	785.9	1003.9	1407.3	1952.8	3655.3	7919.8
63	14723	518.4	589.9	691.2	811.6	1036.8	1453.4	2016.9	3775.2	8179.5
65	15191	534.9	608.6	713.2	837.4	1069.8	1499.6	2080.9	3895.0	8439.2
67	15658	551.3	627.3	735.1	863.2	1102.7	1545.7	2144.9	4014.8	8698.8
69	16125	567.8	646.0	757.1	888.9	1135.6	1591.8	2208.9	4134.7	8958.5
71	16593	584.3	664.8	779.0	914.7	1168.5	1638.0	2273.0	4254.5	9218.2
73	17060	600.7	683.5	800.9	940.5	1201.4	1684.1	2337.0	4374.4	9477.8
75	17528	617.2	702.2	822.9	966.2	1234.3	1730.3	2401.0	4494.2	9737.5
77	17995	633.6	720.9	844.8	992.0	1267.2	1776.4	2465.1	4614.1	9997.2
79	18462	650.1	739.7	866.8	1017.8	1300.2	1822.5	2529.1	4733.9	10256.8
81	18930	666.5	758.4	888.7	1043.5	1333.1	1868.7	2593.1	4853.8	10516.5
83	19397	683.0	777.1	910.7	1069.3	1366.0	1914.8	2657.1	4973.6	10776.2
85	19865	699.5	795.9	932.6	1095.1	1398.9	1961.0	2721.2	5093.5	11035.8
87	20332	715.9	814.6	954.5	1120.8	1431.8	2007.1	2785.2	5213.3	11295.5

Just measure what footage you have available and consult the chart to find a near match on all or the particular
bands of interest. A coaxial cable feed line with no tuner will
suffice if the actual footages of your choices are very close

and you've installed the single QW's on the short side. To get the full use of all of the HF bands, however, use ladder line and a <u>real</u> tuner.

A further option is to end feed the long wire through a line tuner if your matchbox is so configured and a good RF ground is provided at the station. Coaxial cable with the shield grounded at both ends provides the shielded single wire feed. This is necessary due to high voltages appearing on this line.

The advantage of the single wire feed is that it replaces the multiple single quarter wave sections of the dipole at the feed point, but they are still there in the right grounding system.

Notes on the Chart and its use:

The calculations are based on a Velocity Factor of .95, like the formula applied to calculate a simple dipole (L=468/f). It applies to bare antenna wire of copper or copper-clad steel. If you plan to use insulated wire, the lengths in the table will be 1 to 3% too long, depending on the type of insulation. This correction can be ignored if a tuner is used.

Feel free to change the suggested frequency in any band to your ideal choice of center frequency on that band. For example, 2571/3.8=677.4 ft for 11 quarter waves at 3.8 MHz instead of 659.2 ft at 3.9 MHz. This might be needed for a coax feed line, where the SWR curves for the bands involved would be less than flat, narrowing the transmitter's useful bandwidth.

The shaded lengths in the 600-foot category illustrate an almost ideal solution near 650 feet where a length correction of less than 5% on all nine bands is possible. This is easily accomplished electrically with a tube rig or a wide range tuner. It is possible to find a set of lengths at given frequencies to operate even with a built-in tuner into a coaxial feed line.

Better yet, picture a 650 foot long wire with single 1/4 wave short sides fed from a tuner with ladder line as long as 100 feet, working all 9 bands with less than 0.2 dB loss on any HF band, with low SWR! Try one if you can!

ALL-BAND ANTENNAS
and/or
DUMMY LOADS!

Often, we are offered "all-band" antennas that don't require tuners or matching systems. We also learn, from earning our amateur license and from paying attention to our peers and "Elmers." that the only way to ensure the maximum transference of RF power into an antenna is to supply a "load" that satisfies the transceiving system at a given frequency. This condition is referred to as a "**conjugate match**," which can be obtained with an antenna cut to an exact electrical length for a **specific frequency** in a given location connected to the transceiver by an appropriate feed line.

These matching conditions also can be met with a "**dummy load**," which does the same job with a special (non-inductive) resistor big enough to accommodate the transmitted output power. The main purpose of this device is to allow the transceiver to be tuned or matched to a specific load (50 ohms in almost any amateur situation) at any specific frequency without placing a significant signal on the air. The power poured into a dummy load is dissipated as heat, just like electric power poured into a toaster. Radio Frequency power is measured in the same terms but is dissipated in space to a degree related to a calculated **radiation resistance** as well as into the resistance in the metal wire in cable, tubes, transistors and other components. The level of efficiency in RF signals poured into the atmosphere is governed by the level of radiation resistance presented by an antenna, compared to all other resistance in the system.

Now we have to go back to the basics and review the differences in the word "resistance," since at Radio Frequencies it's called **impedance,** which is defined as the complex combination of resistance and reactance in the system. Almost all of the equipment and accessories we use are designed to operate into 50 ohms of impedance. While in matched operation, none of the components cares which, just as long as the sum is close to 50 ohms. The feed line offers resistance due to the characteristic per foot resistance of its conductors, which affects current flow, and, to a lesser degree, the dielectric impedance, which affects voltage and line loss. The total resistance or impedance of the antenna is usually the big variable, since it is different at _every_ frequency, whether the antenna was cut to a tight design specification or cut to the distance between the house and the oak tree.

This variance must be dealt with by equipment tolerance or by matching with a tuner. In operation, the variance appears while tuning up, by automatic or manual means, when the operator or the transceiver itself senses the SWR with a small test signal. The transmitted signal, upon entering the feed line, instantly sees a reactance that is an aggregate of the effect of the feed line _and_ the antenna. Most of today's rigs are solid state (no tubes) and will deny or seriously cut back power output as the SWR ratio increases. Some have built-in tuners (we call them "kinda tuners") that will attempt to correct the mismatch. Such a tuner will succeed if the antenna was designed and built to operate at or near the frequency of choice. One exception is a super long feed line of inadequate coax, which can attenuate the signal to a mismatched antenna so badly that the transceiver sees a near-dummy load with a low SWR and mistakes it as a matched system. The rig then will, if told, pour in full power, the great majority of which will just warm the coax.

Back in the days when all rigs were tube driven, the tolerable mismatch was much greater and the SWR, when observed at all, became apparent only when the tube finals became very hot and/or when the distant operator advised the operator that his signal was poor, or the antenna was down or lost to the weather.

A real tuner, manual or automatic, and depending on its design and the size and quality of its components, can match almost any antenna system of sufficient size at some range of frequency within all of the HF bands _if the feed line is a type of open balanced line._

The size of an antenna has major bearing on the amount of radiation resistance presented. The more wire and/or tubing, the more signal is radiated or received. The most efficient use of the transceiver is into a matched system at an acceptable SWR. The use of balanced line (ladder line) is the icing on the cake at HF and the means to maximum output and input for any HF antenna. Coax from a random size antenna will present such a high SWR at some frequencies that, even if matched with an excellent tuner, the line loss would be horrendous. Larger and better coax can lower this loss, but the cost would be over ten times more than ladder line.

Now, recall the two ways mentioned on page 5.11 for dispersion of an HF signal – a "dummy load" or a system where there was radiation resistance whereby the signal takes off into space where it belongs. Either will handle all the power when matched. The dummy load converts most of the signal to heat, but RF is like light – it's very hard to contain. Many times one will find that he can enjoy a QSO at a good distance even though he forgot to switch from "dummy load" to antenna. If a tiny fraction of a 1-3 watt tune up signal is dissipated into radiation resistance, it will be heard at that frequency from a receiver, miles away. Not too good for DX or a rag chew overseas, but interesting – do you really think you need an amplifier to enjoy the hobby?

And finally, back to the "All Band" antennas on the market. *We've just found that you have one already – your "dummy load!"* Just put it across the feed point of your any length wire antenna up on the roof, and transmit at any frequency into it at its full rated power. You always will have a perfect match – a perfect 1:1 SWR, with no tuner, and you'll make contacts somewhere on HF every time you turn on the rig, honest! Perhaps you can even improve performance by making the dummy load a bit more leaky by using one with a big metallic heat sink instead of oil in a tin can. Your SWR will still stay under 2:1 most anywhere.

Or, if all else fails, you can spend a hundred dollars or more and buy one of the "All Band" dipoles on the market. Then, measure the DC resistance across the output. A reading of 50 ohms or so will assure you that it will work at least as well as your dummy load!

Ask an old ham about the *"ALLBAND"* antenna matcher that swished through the field some years ago! These devices were good for RFI problems in the neighborhood – they attenuated the signal enough to cure the complaints! This, and many "All Band" antennas, can perhaps be defined more accurately as "Leaky Dummy Loads" for the birds!

Dang!
They're toasting
marshmallows on the
all-band matcher
again

Such devices do have merit, however, and we strongly recommend them for the operators who have never learned the merits of the 6th "Ham Commandment." (page 103)

We strongly recommend, for the maximum pleasure in HF operation in our great hobby, a station that includes, in addition to any kind of a transmit/receive setup (including a "dummy load"), a manually adjustable free standing tuner, and a balanced feed line to a dipole of any size, the bigger the better. You'll never lack for contacts, and you'll learn much more about what makes it all work!

Just for fun, some evening when you are enjoying a rag chew with a friend a hundred or so miles away, see how little power you can both use and still understand each other. That may or may not be a surprise, but then try it at full power with your antenna switch turned to your dummy load. If you're on CW, I'd be surprised if you couldn't copy and be heard with ease. Even SSB might make it. TRY IT!

Years ago, in a high school gym in Michigan, our yearly Novice class had a "live" night in the middle of the 10 week course, to which the parents or friends were invited. We set up an old HW-16 station on the table connected to a dummy load, tuned to a novice band frequency, and listened to the static at low volume as we started that week's lesson on antennas.

After a discussion of fundamentals, including matching, dipoles, SWR, etc., it came to "show and tell" time, and the kids showed off their prowess, or lack of it, with the straight key at 5 WPM and about 1 watt.

A scrap-box of scrap wire supplied a few pieces of random length wire, which, when connected to the antenna terminal via a length of coax, provided the means to demonstrate resonant length and matching. Bicycles were connected to the end of each wire.

Finally, after switching to the antenna system, a mass of slow CW could be heard, and one of the better students was invited to try sending a CQ. He was promptly answered by a local ham (Sure, it was a setup!), to the delight of all.

The end of the lesson illustrated the need for proper tune up procedure by returning to the dummy load and disconnecting the antenna completely. The QSO continued with no problem!

We live with the fond hope that none of our students who earned their tickets have ever been heard on the bands while tuning up! (Well, almost never!)

If you learn nothing else from this exercise, I hope you'll now avoid tuning up right on the net frequency even if you're on the dummy load. Those irritating "tuner-uppers" you hear are often the good guys, who mistakenly think their signal is going totally into the "can," or think that 1 watt won't radiate from the antenna!

Looks like N8UG is in for his annual checkup!
(Probably has "writer's cramp!)

We could cure him if we could get to him!

Antenna Sag Determination

Nomograph[6] instructions

1. Lay the nomograph on a flat surface or make a copy of it with a scanner or copier so that you can work with it. You will need a simple straight edge about 6 inches long.
2. **Consult the wire tables for the weight per 1000 feet, Break Strength and recommended tension figures for the wire of interest.**
3. Lay the straight edge on the nomograph, intersecting the weight of 1000 ft of the antenna wire of your choice and the span of wire you intend to use. Remember, the span is defined, in this case, as **one half of the distance between supports.**
4. Make a mark or hold a sharp point at the point at which the straight edge crosses the work axis.
5. Rotate the straight edge on that point until the left end rests on the recommended tension for the wire[7].
6. Read the sag in feet on the sag column.
7. Consider the year round conditions at your QTH and assay the effects of ice, high wind, and, if applicable, the weight of a center insulator and feed line if you are stuck with the problem of no center support.

Need an example?

Weight of wire = 11 pounds per 1000 feet
Span = 210 feet (1/2 of 420 ft total between supports)
Rotate straightedge on work axis~
Tension = 50 pounds
Read: Sag = 4.7 feet

Note that if you hang a feed line from a center insulator in this example, adding about 9 pounds, the sag would increase to nearly 8 feet, diminishing performance. See *The Ubiquitous Dipole,* page 146, for center support ideas.

---

[6] Thanks to the ARRL, with permission, and credit to the author, W1DQ.
[7] Lots of variables here – consult the wire charts and related discussion.

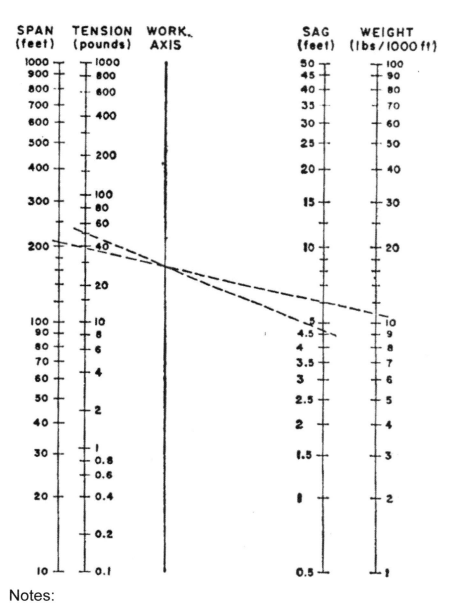

Notes:

_____
_____
_____
_____

ROPE

A top quality rope is an essential accessory in amateur radio for a variety of reasons, from dipole support to erecting towers and antennas, hoisting, and pulling cables.

There are at least as many types of rope as there are types of wire and cable, but, as usual there are good, better and best choices for different jobs.

Synthetic ropes are best for most of our work because they are stronger and more durable than natural fiber types, and have greater resistance to abrasion, rot, mildew, and most chemicals. They also have low absorption of water, and selected types have excellent resistance to damage from the sun (ultra-violet light).

Combination ropes that utilize the best characteristics of different styles and constructions offer the best choice, and over 25 years, **Dacron**®[8] polyester double braid has become the favorite of the amateur community. We have samples of the various sizes that have endured over 30 years of exposure to sun and weight with no deterioration, bolstering our confidence in this material. The outer braid is a dense black double weave for high UV and abrasion resistance, while the inner braid is white polyester, of a more lineal pattern for high strength with minimal stretch. The weave or braid is a neutral "lay" – no spiral – so there is no twisting in pulleys or when sliding over limbs.

Kevlar®[1] is another popular synthetic material of even greater strength that is used alone or in combination with other synthetics. Typically, it is more costly, but enterprising hams often find it in military and other surplus sources at bargain prices. It is stronger than polyester, and less subject to damage from gas and oil. It is, however, rated lower in resistance to abrasion, ultraviolet, and acid. Of greater importance to amateurs, though, is that it has lower shock strength, size for size. This could be most significant when a section of tower gets away while being raised or lowered and is stopped suddenly by a secured rope.

---

[8] Registered trademarks of Dupont, Inc.

Attention should be paid to *Break Strength* as well as recommended *Working Load* of all sizes of rope when selecting the one for each job. The *Working Load* figure will be *some* fraction of the *Break Strength,* usually expressed in percent, and will vary widely among the materials used, from as low as 20% to nearly 50%. Manufacturers are very cautious about these figures, since they vary wildly depending on whether the pull is straight or at an angle, smooth or jerky, over a flat or curved pulley wheel of a proper diameter, at what acceleration, etc, etc.

Get the picture? Select the best one for you and don't bother to even consider going after a manufacturer if it breaks!

From our experience, you cannot do better than the popular black polyester double braided rope so readily available in the amateur marketplace. The samples we set out in the hot South Carolina sun under load in the early '80's are still there, in good condition. Personally, I use scraps of the 3/32-inch type for my boot laces – makes the high-priced stuff from the shoe store look sick!

He keeps muttering something about "The Woodpecker on 80?"

Anyone remember?

Baluns

As I said in **Wirebook IV**, "This is a whale of a subject, and there are so many authoritative writings out there on the subject that it is quite presumptive for us to comment." Still true!

We will begin this time by defining the playing field. I am a filter, gatherer, and a student. RF transformers and baluns are one of my favorite subjects. I am truly blessed by friendship with good friends who have a wealth of knowledge in this field, so when questions come to **The Wireman** on this or any subject, my answers come from the pool of information gleaned from their collective brains over the years. I'm not an authority who has tested every hypothesis, but I can often help answer your questions, and you'll have the benefit of the expertise of a group of the best minds available!

Do I need one?

The most frequent question on the subject is, "Do I need one?" Most of the time the answer is, ". . . possibly, but tell me about your system."

Consider the name "bal - un", derived from balanced - unbalanced, and you're on the way to understanding what it's all about. In the case of balanced line, two equal conductors carry the oscillations of a radio frequency signal from a transceiver, through a matching device (tuner), to an antenna feed point, where the signal goes equally to each side of the antenna.

If the transmission line is coaxial cable, the scenario is the same, but the result differs, as you might expect, since the two conductors are not the same. One is a single solid or stranded wire, and the other a tube, so to speak, of braid or foil. The latter braid or foil is normally RF grounded at some point(s) in the system. These criteria make this an unbalanced line. The center conductor surface-traveling signal, upon reaching the feed point, again finds its way to one side of the antenna. The portion of the signal traveling up on the inside surface of the braid, however, finds that it has a choice at the feed point. It can enter the antenna, or, it can travel down the outside of the braid, or both. Most of the signal follows the path of least resistance, into the antenna, but some signal does appear on the outside of the braid. It has no confines there, so it radiates. (fig. 1)

If a feed line does not radiate, there will not be coupling with adjacent wires and cables, tower legs, etc., nor will it be

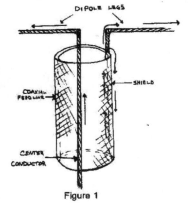

Figure 1

a source of RFI. Further, the radiation pattern of the antenna will not be compromised by such coupling or conflicting radiation. This very well may be a non-problem in a lower power station.

Enter the balun. Placed at the feed point, it becomes an RF choke, blocking the path leading back down the outside of the coax. The balun can be a wound device using an iron powder toroid, ferrite rod or toroid, or air as a core. It can be a coil of the coax feed line itself. It can be a series of ferrite beads, but the function is the same.

This sounds like a strong case for the balun, and it does sell a lot of them, but before you rip down your dipole or build a new one, look over your situation and, "If it ain't broke, don't fix it." There are just as many reasons why **not** to use a balun, so it behooves you to look carefully at your station or your plans, such as working a single net every day, or just enjoying a rag chew with friends on a regular schedule at a regular frequency. The need for a balun might be nil with a matched system and a flat SWR.

Another example: A simple dipole cut for the center of the band and you roam at will from one end to the other. Neither your family nor your neighbors have ever heard or seen your signals in their stereo, phone or TV. Your system is well made and well matched, and your operating power is 100 watts, maximum. *It would make no sense to take it down and install a balun.*

If the situation on your part is the same, but you are bothering people with RFI, TVI, the works, then maybe it is time for a balun. But first, you should take time for a few observations:

Check your RF ground (see "Station grounding")

Check your equipment. Do any of the problems occur when you transmit into a dummy load? Analyze the complaint. The problem could be with one neighbor's antique TV antenna, or with everyone in the neighborhood due to a fault in the cable TV distribution system. RFI is a big subject, only partially related to this discussion. Look for more in this area elsewhere in the book, or pick up the **ARRL *RFI BOOK*[1]**, it's a good one.

At this point, you might be able to forget the balun, having found a more probable cause. If you still feel the need, however, try the coiled coax idea (See page 173) If it makes a difference, then shop for or make a balun – but read up on

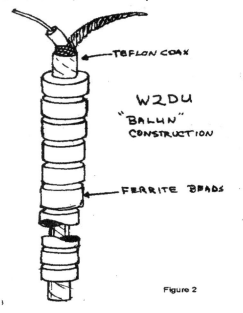

the W2DU type (fig. 2). It is a simple choke type current balun (or "balun eliminator") that will do it all with no effect of length or complexity to the antenna. Also it will easily handle full legal power in a matched system. The best technical discussion of this item can be found in QST, March 1983, "*Some Aspects of the Balun Problem*," by Walt Maxwell, W2DU, or if you want all the straight dope you'll ever need, get a copy of Walt's new book, ***REFLECTIONSIII*.**[2]

Take note! If you do elect to install a balun, don't do it to improve your SWR. The balun has nothing to do with it. If

---

[1] The ARRL RFI Book, First Edition, The American Radio Relay League, #235.

[2] Maxwell, Walter, REFLECTIONS, ARRL. 1990; REFLECTIONS II, WorldRadio Books, 2001, REFLECTIONS III, CQ Communications 2009..

your antenna does not present an acceptable load to your transceiver, you need to correct the antenna or put in a tuner, or both.

Note in your study of the W2DU balun that no coils of wire are involved. It's a choke and a short extension of the feed line, that's all. If you need a balun in that sense of the word (balanced to unbalanced via a choke), it works great.

Other balun considerations relate to the transformation needed to match a feed line to a higher or lower impedance antenna feed point such as in a folded dipole, Windom, quad, or loop. They are utilized in tuners and matching networks to expand their capability, and are known as **balun transformers or un-un transformers**, referring to their dual function.

Summarizing, *the balun, as we know it in amateur radio, matches equal and unequal impedances in a signal path in balanced, unbalanced, or mixed condition, thereby maximizing the signal that reaches the targeted load and minimizing the loss of signal outside of the intended path.*

There are lots of calls on this subject, and even more since the W2DU baluns appeared on the scene. They became popular for several reasons. They are easy to understand, easy to build, inexpensive for the do-it-yourselfer, and above all, they work with excellence for the purpose for which they were designed.

Like many of the situations in radio, there is no one answer to all of the questions. If you understand some of the basic differences as they apply to amateur usage you may be able to make your choice wisely.

Voltage baluns are designed to equalize the voltage in each side or leg of an antenna, whereas the current balun balances the current flow. It becomes immediately obvious that the current type balun is superior at an antenna feed point, since RF current balance and magnitude are the criteria for top performance of an antenna.

Voltage baluns are often wound or configured as an autotransformer. This style has been employed very successfully for years in, and in conjunction with, unbalanced tuners for matching to balanced transmission lines such as ladder line. This works quite well in amateur setups with random length antennas with random length balanced feed lines matched by a good tuner for all-band (HF) operation that can, with the aid of the balun transformer, deal with the wide range of reactance presented by the antenna system.

Baluns of this type have often received a bad rap in recent years due to the proliferation of a new generation of inexpensive analyzers in the amateur community. These devices easily show what has always been there, that an auto-transformer's performance into a pure resistive load will show a whole range of *Standing Wave Ratios* as one moves across all of the HF bands. This is true, of course, but not relevant, since the load presented by the whole system to the tuner is what is brought to a *conjugate match* for the maximum transference of power into the load. Further, as many operators of such systems can attest, the matchbox or tuner that does the job at any given frequency keeps its "cool," proving, without benefit of instrumentation, that the efficiency is certainly acceptable. *"Low Heat, Low Loss!"*

A better approach for these antennas is a better tuner, with components that can deal with a wider range of reactance, making the 4:1 transformer unnecessary. Several such tuners are now available with a husky 1:1 current balun to handle the balancing chore.

The 1:1 current or choke type balun supplies a stopping or choking resistance only to the small fraction of the RF current that tries to travel back on the outside of the coaxial feed line, thus forcing almost all of the RF current equally into the two sides of the antenna. This function is not nearly as frequency sensitive in the current balun. Since heavy-duty components are not required, full power handling capability is available.

It should be noted here that the 4:1 choke-type or bead balun is configured in series/parallel, and while very effective, it is not capable of handling the high power that a well-designed toroid-type powdered iron, or ferrite voltage or current balun can.

The Coaxial Cable Balun

The coaxial balun is big, awkward and ugly but it's cheap and works very well if done correctly. The coax balun is a current-type device that has been suggested by antenna manufacturers for years as an effective choke to keep RF off of the feed line and thus control RFI while maximizing the performance of the antenna. Unfortunately, the usual instruction is to, "...make up a plus or minus 9 turn bundle of TX line right at the antenna, tape it up and tie it to the mast ...," or words to that effect. The random bundle is very likely at least a partial waste of time and cable since the odds of the RF on the first and last turns coupling directly are such that the best you can hope for is the effect gained by half of whatever number of turns that you use[3]. So, *"Do it right or forget it,"* is our advice. The drawing illustrates the correct way for maximum effect. Use solid dielectric 50 ohm coax with at least a Class IIA jacket, of a size that will handle your power level with ease. Keep the turns tight. Strive for 100%

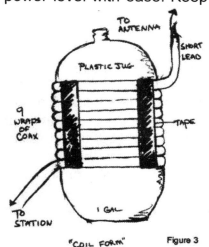

contact between each. Pay attention to the minimum diameter rule for the choice of form $(15 \times OD)$[4] if you plan to make it permanent. You can use a jug for a form (for RG 8) and remove it, or leave it in place as a hanger and perhaps a conversation piece. The neighbors will assume that it's party time, perhaps! Or consider the W2DU current balun (P/N 827) lightweight, inconspicuous, and effective, and it does the same job a bit better, custom made to your spec's.

Figure 3

The W2DU "balun" - Pro and Con
A Chat With Walt

In the past year we have observed conflicting information in the amateur community, our correspondence, and various radio amateur oriented "reflectors" on the Internet regarding the performance of ferrite bead "baluns." The discussions have involved the choice of ferrites, the number of beads

---

[3]Recent data from several investigators have proven this point.
[4]RG 58, .197 X 15 = ~3"diameter; RG 8, .405 X 15 = 6" diameter; etc.

deployed, power tolerance, and even the wisdom of using such a device.

These devices have been somewhat of a phenomenon in our hobby, and, as one of the leading vendors of them for nearly 20 years, we feel qualified to offer some background information that should be considered by those involved or interested.

Walt Maxwell, W2DU, is the designer and creator of this type of balun, and he did so with his many years of expertise in the field and thorough research and development with the device itself before introducing it QST in March 1983. Further reference came in Walt's book, *"Reflections"*, then *"Reflections II"* , and now, *"Reflections III"*

Following the introduction in 1983, Walt licensed the Microwave Filter Corp. to make and supply the balun to the amateur community. Later, Microwave Filter Corp. sold its Unadilla Amateur Division, and the new owner continued making the W2DU balun without a license. At about the same time The Wireman began making the W2DU balun with a license. Since then, The Wireman has gone through several million of the 73-type beads and a lesser number of the 43-types (for VHF). The annual usage continues to rise, as do the requests for advice and information regarding all facets of the application, including criticisms, constructive and otherwise.

When the queries include destructive criticism, there is an immediate need for re-examination, whether the item is a "flash in the pan" or a well-established, successful commodity that really works. So saying, we have asked Walt to discuss the background of his experimentation with the ferrite bead balun so that we can better understand it and its applications and performance.

Walt has obliged with a thorough review of the subject, and we were pleased and proud to include it in "Wirebook IV." We urge all curious amateurs to read it and learn why the W2DU "balun" has enjoyed great success for nearly 30 years. Walt's comments begin on the next page.

We find it difficult to panic over the few negative outbursts in the past year and a few reports from well-respected experts in the field who offered worst-case, seldom occurring scenarios that could tend to make users and potential users wary. We prefer, and encourage others who ask, to use the parameters and materials that W2DU laid out as a result of his extensive work and subsequent proofing. The short cuts, different bead counts, and substitutions suggested have the flavor of anecdotal advice and opinion without documentation or intensive research such as that done by the originator.

At 50 beads per "balun," our records show that we alone have been responsible for at least 40,000 W2DU bead "baluns" either built by us or by amateurs who have bought the "fixins" from us and "rolled their own."

We cannot guess how many have been made by others, or how many liberties have been taken with the W2DU formula for quantity of beads and type of mix. We do know, for example, of an HF "Beam Balun" on the market that contains only twenty five #73 beads instead of at least 50, reducing the cost, but also reducing the longitudinal impedance to only half that which W2DU specified as required to obtain the necessary reduction of outer conductor current. Obviously, this short-changing of material increases the longitudinal current through the beads as opposed to using a sufficient bead quantity to minimize the current and the attendant rise in temperature.

As a vendor who is very sensitive to criticism, constructive or otherwise, we always have solicited comment from any users of our products. As a result, all of our "CQ Originals" are the product of amateur needs, either real or perceived. Some of the ideas have "bombed." Some have required major re-inventing, but the W2DU "balun" has enjoyed spectacular success and minimal failure for over 25 years and counting. Specifically, we have done less than ten "autopsies" on real or imagined failures over the years, and NONE of them have been caused by up to full legal power in a resonant system.

A recent commentary also describes failures due to construction errors, and suggests that the W2DU's as a whole are defective. There are many copy-cats out there whose work may or may not follow the standards approved by Walt, and these "just as good" versions should not be used to judge the legitimate originals. We amateurs are, by nature, quick to react when stuck with a "lemon," or an item that fails within the parameters of the claimed specifications. The track record of the real W2DU balun indicates that it has done its job with excellence for years. This is the proof we need, not the prognostications of what "could" happen.

"Let the buyer beware," is an old suggestion which still has merit, and a simple query as to whether the vendor is licensed to call his product a "W2DU" device might well be prudent in these competitive times.

The following are Walt's own words:

"The problem reported from using W2DU-type baluns made by some manufacturers is overheating. So let's examine the reasons for the problem to arrive at an understanding that can assist in correcting the problem. To begin, we know that the current flowing on the inner surface of the outer conductor of the transmission line divides at the antenna terminals, one part flowing onto the dipole half connected to the outer conductor, the other part flowing down the outer surface of the outer conductor. The division of currents in this parallel circuit is dependent on the relative impedances of the two current paths. The current flowing on the outer conductor is dependent on the longitudinal impedance of the path and the voltage applied to it. The impedance of the outer conductor path is determined by three parameters; 1) the ground resistance at the point where the feed line connects to the effective electrical ground through the transceiver to the power line ground; 2) the electrical length of the outer conductor of the feed line; and 3) the longitudinal impedance of the balun, if any, in series with the longitudinal impedance of the outer surface of the feed line that appears at the source end of the balun.

"Let's first consider the voltage applied to the outer conductor path. One half of the voltage appearing at the antenna terminals appears across the parallel impedance at the junction of the dipole half and the outer conductor of the feed line. The voltage across the outer conductor path appears between the fore-mentioned junction and the entire length of the outer conductor of the feed line terminating at the effective electrical ground. Consequently, the voltage appearing across the balun, if any, is the total outer path voltage less the voltage appearing on the outer surface of the line itself. It then follows that the power dissipated in the balun is the product of the current through the outer path and the voltage appearing only longitudinally across the balun.

"Let's now consider an unrealizable worst case for the impedance of the outside surface of the outer conductor by making several hypothetical assumptions. First, let's assume the outer conductor is terminated in perfect ground; second, the outer conductor is an exact multiple of a half-wavelength, and third, assume that there is no radiation from the conductor. With these assumptions the source end of the balun would be at perfect ground potential, and half the voltage appearing at the antenna terminals would indeed appear across the longitudinal impedance of the balun alone, as some have claimed.

"But in reality this is not the case. In reality the effective ground resistance obtained via the power line ground is a very poor ground at RF, which can run into several hundred ohms for the termination of the outer conductor to be reflected back to the source end of the balun. In addition, the feed line radiates energy resulting from any current flowing on it, however small, which further increases the longitudinal impedance on the outer surface seen at the source end of the balun. Furthermore, if the length of the outer surface of the feed line to ground were an odd multiple of a quarter wavelength the longitudinal impedance seen at the source end of the balun would be several thousand ohms regardless of the ground resistance and any radiation from the outer surface. For lengths other than multiples of a half wavelength the reactance increases sharply, thus greatly impeding the current flow from that occurring when the length is exactly a multiple of a half wavelength.

"Let's now examine the criteria I used in engineering the bead balun to determine the actual longitudinal impedance of the balun. This examination allows us to determine the operating power and SWR limits for certain design parameters. We will thus discover that many cases of overheating result only from exceeding the power and SWR limits for a given configuration, and not from the generic W2DU type of bead balun.

"My reasoning began with a given that the longitudinal impedance of a bead string should be no less than ten times the half-dipole impedance of the driven element. I further reasoned that for a general-purpose balun for use from 2 – 30 MHz, the worst practical case appeared to occur with an 80-m dipole at around 40' above ground operating at 3.5 MHz when resonant at 3.75 MHz. At resonance the terminal impedance of this dipole is around 65 + j0 ohms, and around 53 − j123 ohms at 3.5 MHz, for an impedance approximately 135 ohms, and an SWR approximately 7.5:1 relative to 50 ohms. (These are **measured** data that can be found in Reflections I Page 15-19, in Reflections II, Page 15-14 and in Chapter 15 on W2DU's web page at http:/home.iag.net/~w2du.) The measured longitudinal impedance versus frequency of two bead configurations is shown in Fig 21-3 in both editions of Reflections, and in Chapter 21 on the web page. The impedance plot for 50 #73 beads is shown for the range 2 - 30 MHz and for 25 #43 beads for the range 30 - 250 MHz. (These are the configurations employed by The Wireman.)

"From Fig 21-3 it can be seen that the longitudinal bead impedance at 3.5 MHz is approximately 1100 ohms. With the half-dipole impedance of approximately 68 ohms (135 ÷ 2) the bead impedance is seen to be 16 times greater than the half-dipole impedance. We'll now calculate the power dissipated in the balun at 3.5 MHz where the SWR is 7.5:1 and the radiated power is approximately 1 kw. When the line is matched to 50 ohms the line voltage is 223.6 volts for a forward power of 1 kw. With the antenna mismatch of 7.5:1 the forward power increase factor is 2.408 for 1 kw absorbed by the antenna, for a forward power of 2408 watts, (reflected power is 1408 watts) and a forward voltage increase factor of 1.55, making the actual voltage appearing the antenna terminals 346.6 volts. The half voltage appearing across the total longitudinal impedance of the feed line is thus 173.3 volts. Assuming now the unrealistic hypothetical worst case where the entire half voltage appears across the 1100-ohm longitudinal impedance of the balun alone, the current is 0.16 a. and the power dissipated in the balun is 27.3 watts. However, under realistic conditions with the far-from-zero effective ground resistance, plus radiation from the feed line, and the unlikely chance that the electrical length of the feed line is near a multiple of a half wavelength, current along the outer surface of the line is significantly less than if the voltage appeared only across the longitudinal impedance of the balun. Thus the actual dissipation in the balun is significantly less than 27 watts. In addition, with the balun in open air the temperature rise in the ferrite beads will not rise to a level sufficient to damage the beads.

"Now to some measurements that prove The Wireman's product should not break down during operation within the conditions specified. I tested a #73-mix 50-bead balun under the conditions just described above with key down periods of 15 minutes (with appropriate call sign ID during the tests). The feed line was one half wavelength from the antenna tuner to the antenna terminals. The distance from the tuner through the transceiver to the power line ground was around 20 to 25 feet. After repeated tests no changes were observed in the impedance of the bead string--no bead failures.

"At 14 MHz the bead impedance is approximately 1300 ohms. Assuming a worst case of a 3:1 SWR on 20m, with 1.3333 kw of forward power for 1 kw radiated power, the voltage at the antenna terminals is 260 volts. Half of this voltage, 130 volts appears across the longitudinal impedance of the entire balun-feed-line combination. Again assuming the unrealistic hypothetical worst case where the entire half voltage appears only across the longitudinal impedance of the balun, the current is 0.11 a. and the power dissipated in the balun is 13.0 watts. But again, under realistic conditions the power dissipated in the balun is significantly less than 13 watts. Considering the surface area of the bead string this small amount of dissipation cannot cause a temperature rise sufficient to result in breakdown."

"It must be kept in mind that the powers dissipated in the balun as calculated above is in key-down condition--100 percent duty cycle, which is the worst case except in RTTY use. With the shorter duty cycles of SSB and CW it is obvious that the power dissipated is less that that indicated in the calculations above. If the baluns manufactured by The Wireman are used in accordance with the operating conditions described above there should be no problem of damage to the beads due to overheating."

Our never ending thanks to W2DU for his fine works and counsel continues as we pass his skills on to our fellow Hams in the form of his famous "bead baluns" in multiple models and kits. We urge our friends in the hobby that want the "straight dope" to consider his "REFLECTIONS III" for their Amateur Radio library. It will be available from The Wireman, CQ Amateur Radio, and most other dealers before the 4th of July 2009.

Chapter 10 - Great Antenna Stories From All Over!

Over the years, we've supplied many antenna builders with materials, especially antenna wire and ladderline feeders, and the feedback from the many amateurs has been a great experience. It represents a rebirth of what used to be the only way to carry an HF RF signal from the shack to the antenna! Coaxial cable, for this purpose, is too expensive, too difficult to work full bandwidth, and never as efficient. Further, coax fails to enrich the knowledge and under-standing so important to the total value of amateur radio in our quest to understand the basics!.

We hope that sharing the experiences of Hams who have realized the pleasure, satisfaction, and pride in the building and use of these antennas.

We strongly urge those of you that have the space and want to get serious about this approach, to look at these examples and the detailed proof following the stories.

Here's W7RF's great near 1100 foot horizontal loop story in his own words. WM's proud to have had a hand in it!

"Approx 1050' of wire in an (almost) square horizontal loop up 65 feet.

I would like to share with you and the readers of your Wireman book, the details of design, construction, installation, operation, and performance of the loop.

To describe it's performance in a few words would be to quote my most frequent statement, '*it performs like a Yagi in all directions!*'

I started planning this antenna when the thought of what I might install on my new property was just that, a thought. We moved from Los Angeles in April 2007 to Fort Collins, CO on 3 acres, shaped 450' deep x 300' wide.In LA, we lived on a standard lot of 55' x 110', so when looking through the antenna books, there were many pages of antennas that were only a fantasy.

A large loop was one of them.

With the help of the late L.B Cebik W4RNL, we chatted for a few months over e-mail honing the individual parameters of what came to be my loop.

The design parameters were quite basic, put up as large of a loop of wire as high as possible, I'm a Dxer and used to big Yagi's in my previous location, so I wanted a good signal everywhere. I decided on 2 WL at the lowest frequency of 160M because 1 WL at only 65 feet would be a cloud burner, 2 WL and greater is where the lobes start to "fold" onto each other and provide a lower angle of radiation than the height of 65 feet would dictate.

The number of wavelengths of wire goes up and up from 160M as you get higher in frequency. For example, on 20M it's about 14 wavelengths long! On 20M Gain is over 10 db in peak lobe directions and the horizontal pattern is quite full with multiple "spikes" of gain in points all around the 360 degree azimuth. Angle of radiation is very low as the 1 wavelength height is further enhanced by the "lobe folding in" properties of multiple wavelengths of wire. All of this varies in exactness by band.

During the Summer of 2008, when we had prolonged Solar Flux of 67, I worked all over the globe with great signals on 40M-17M, smashed pileups and beat stations running Yagi antennas! Even 75M European SSB DX was not uncommon during these Summer months!

I used mostly Wireman products, #14 CCS solid antenna wire, fed with #16 stranded 450 ohm ladder line (about 200 feet of Wireman #552), center insulator is a model 803. Each corner I used a ceramic "dog bone" insulator. Each pole has a custom made stainless steel W9IIX constructed 2" wide 1/4" thick stainless steel flat bar with a stainless steel "S" hook to a lifetime lubricated pulley. About 140' of 1/4" uv resistant Dacron rope (wireman #817), is used to raise and lower each corner. I decided to twist each corner wire to make a fixed length of wire from pole to pole for ease of measuring and making taught. I made the wire a few feet shorter than each pole to pole span to allow for ease in raising and making taught. To keep the Dacron rope from slapping in the wind, I simply walk around the pole with the rope twice after making the wire taught and tie off to a galvanized steel cleat on each pole.

The ladder line is soldered to each wire coming out of the 803 center insulator and wrapped with rubber electrical sealing tape and then wrapped with scotch 33+ black electrical tape. This tape system extends for about 6" and provides some strength and flexibility to the feed point.

I feed my loop in one corner but one can feed anywhere along the line from corner to middle of a side. Radiation pattern changes a bit but performance is very similar both ways. Corner feed (actually about 1 foot off one corner) provides better mechanical stability since the weight and components of the feedpoint are supported very close to one pole.

From the feedpoint I run the 450 ladder line down at about a 30 degree angle to the first feedline support pole located about 30 feet away from the feedpoint pole. At this first feed line support pole, I built a spark plug (non-resistor, NGK B8ES) lightning arrestor system inside a weatherproof box from the electrical department of Home Depot and mounted it at about 10 feet off the ground on that pole with a large #4 wire running to a ground rod. The feed line then travels horizontally about 125' to my Ham shack, supported every 30' with 10' steel "TV" masts with 18" of 1" PVC pipe and "T" connectors on top to insulate and support the feedline. Gap the spark plugs to not arc with whatever your maximum power will be, try different frequencies.

The best way to transfer your power into this feedline is through a true balanced tuner, I use the Palstar BT1500A, which is absolutely the highest quality tuner for any balanced line system."

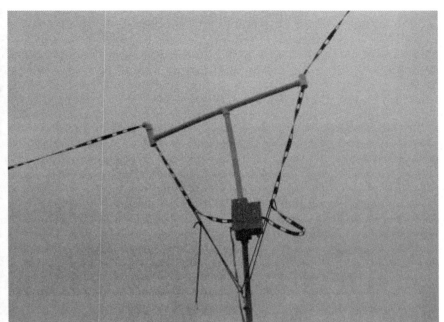

W7RF's loop feedline running from the upper right UV resistant PVC pipe to the box enclosing his homemade spark plug lightning arrestor and beyond through PVC pipe toward the feedpoint (below)

The pole at the feed point (above), showing "Porcupine" lightning dissipater, rope tether, strain relief, corner insulator feed point insulator, and ladderline feeder, bare and sealed.

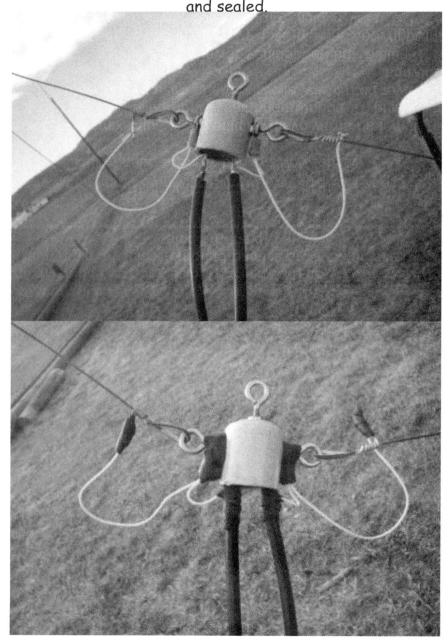

W7RF's QTH at the far right, also the feed point, near his shack in the second building from the right just past the pole,

****

Here is AD4FI's new 80 meter dipole story in his own words. WM's proud to have been helpful!

"I shot an arrow over two pine trees, approximately 80 feet tall, using 12 pound mono line. I then pulled a ¼ inch black line over both trees, allowing me to raise the 80 meter dipole antenna.

I pulled the ladderline down to the shack, pushed it through one inch gray PVC and attached the ends to a 12VDC relay (which grounds both sides of ladderline and dipole when the antenna is not in use). I then attached twin coax lines to the other side of the relay, grounding the shields. I placed both lines into shrink wrap attached them to the outside of the shack, then through a hole to the Palstar tuner inside, where I again grounded the twin shields to the tuner ground and the center conductors to the balanced input terminals.

Thanks Press – best antenna I've ever had!
Ralph R(Bob) Lester, L/T Col. USAF, Fighter Pilot, Retired
AD4FI

Here are photos of the 80 meter dipole using the 450 ohm "window" line that we discussed on the phone."

Feed line from the sky! There's a dipole way up there!
Shows the ladderline entering the PVC "el" at the house

Gray PVC run to relay under eave

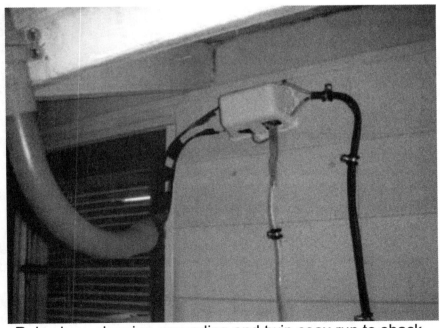

Relay box, showing grounding and twin coax run to shack

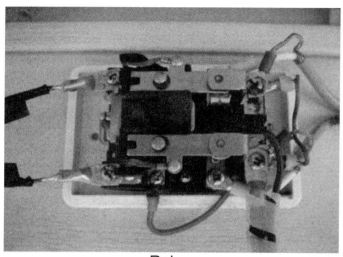

Relay

****

The Long Wire Loop: an Omnidirectional, Multiband, Low Angle Radiator
By Steve Cerwin, WA5FRF

"Introduction: Something Old and Something New

As the name implies, long wire loop is a marriage of the venerable long wire antenna and a horizontal loop. Each antenna has both advantages and disadvantages, but when combined together you get all the advantages of both and the disadvantages of neither. The end result is a multiband antenna that has nearly an omni-directional radiation pattern, presents a friendly low feed impedance at all harmonics (not just the odd ones), and has a very low takeoff angle for excellent DX performance. The mechanism responsible for the low takeoff angle is suppression of vertical radiation, a process commonly used to produce gain on the horizon. The antenna has a feed point that presents a short at DC for elimination of static buildup and rain noise and also provides excellent rejection of out of band signals, making for very quiet receive performance. Added to this is the fact that the antenna is as simple as it is cheap, consisting only of wire and a few supports. So what's the downside? This antenna is BIG. But if you have lots of room the long wire loop is hard to beat from the standpoints of frequency and directional coverage, performance, and cost.

Theory of Operation: A Tale of Two Antennas

I. The Long Wire

Long wire antennas have been around nearly since the inception of radio. Usually configured in straight lines in the fashion of a dipole, these antennas were characterized as having a radiation pattern broken up into lobes, with strong peaks in some directions and deep nulls in others. lithe long wire is operated at a resonant length consisting of an odd number of half wavelengths, the antenna will present a low feed impedance in the center of any one of the half wave sections, and there will be as many lobes on each side of the antenna as there are half wavelengths. On even harmonics, the same feed point presents an unwieldy high impedance and the pattern still breaks into lobes (though with a different schedule). The pattern of a typical long wire antenna is shown in one of the traces in Fig. I . At very long lengths, most of the energy tends to be directed in a small angle off the ends of the wire with less contained in the multi-lobed broadside pattern. This is the effect giving rise to the V-beam and rhombic, but that is another story. Thus as an antenna, the long wire provides "friendly" feed impedances only on odd harmonics and has a radiation pattern that gives excellent coverage in some directions, none in others.

2. The Loop

Loop antennas take on different characteristics depending on how long their circumference is compared to a wavelength. The most common format in amateur practice is a loop with one wavelength circumference. Oriented vertically in a square shape the one-wavelength loop offers a bit over two dB of gain over a dipole. This structure is the building block of the high performance parasitic array known as the quad. As a single element antenna, the vertical one wavelength loop has also found popular service in the triangular format known as the delta loop. In the mid eighty's, Dave Fischer, WOMHS published an article describing a one wavelength square loop oriented horizontally. He dubbed the antenna the "Loop Skywire". This antenna offers several attractive features including an omnidirectional pattern, simplicity, and a feed point presenting a friendly impedance and a short at DC with the attendant low receiving noise. However, this antenna has acquired the reputation of being a "cloud warmer", or high angle radiator. Indeed, as shown in Fig. 2, it has less low angle radiation than a dipole mounted at the same height. Thus the one wavelength horizontal loop performs very well for local or near-vertical incidence work, but not so well as other antenna types for DX where a low takeoff angle is required.

The Long Wire Loop: Longer is Better

One reason the one wavelength horizontal loop has poor low angle performance compared to a dipole is because of the inherent 2.2dB broadside gain of the loop: the antenna wants to direct most of its energy upward. But if operated on the second harmonic (or more), an overhead null is created. Conservation of energy requires the radiation to go somewhere, and if it can't go up, it must go out. Creation of an overhead null is the basic operating principle of most high performance low angle antennas including the pioneering 8JK two-element beam in which two side-by-side dipoles were driven out of phase. Figure 2 contrasts three antenna types mounted at the same operating height: a one wavelength horizontal loop (the Loop Skywire), a dipole, and a two wavelength long wire loop. Low angle performance increases in just this order, with the long wire loop giving a lower takeoff angle than a dipole, which in turn gives a lower takeoff angle than the Loop Skywire. At longer harmonic lengths, the takeoff angle of the long wire loop gets even lower - remarkably so, as shown in Figure 9.

The second area in which a long wire loop shines is in azimuthal coverage. While a long wire antenna gives a pattern that breaks up into lobes, folding the same length of wire into a loop frustrates lobe creation and provides a nearly omnidirectional azimuth pattern. This is illustrated in Fig. 1. which shows the familiar multilobe structure of a traditional lone wire antenna and the nearly uniform pattern of a long wire loop of the same length.Gone are the deep nulls and holes in azimuth coverage. If you have a big antenna that you can't rotate and you want to work anywhere without restriction, the closer you can get to omnidirectional the better.

The way in which the horizontal loop defeats the formation of coverage nulls is worthy of a closer look. Figure 3 shows the horizontal pattern resolved into three field components: horizontal polarization, vertical polarization, and total field. As can be seen in the figure, the horizontal loop produces vertically polarized as well as horizontally polarized radiation. It is not that lobe structures are not formed, but that the vertically polarized pattern is complimentary to the horizontally polarized pattern. One peaks when the other nulls, leaving a total field pattern which is nearly omnidirectional. Since nearly all sky wave propagation randomizes polarization anyway, the fact that the horizontal loop initially radiates horizontal polarization in some directions and vertical in others is of no consequence.

Scaling: When Bigger Just Can't Be

The motivation for the long wire loop admittedly was to garner high performance, omnidirectional coverage on the low frequency bands of 160 through 40 meters, in response to our inexorable slide down the backside of the current sunspot cycle. Thus the antennas described above tend to be big. But that is not to say that the long wire loop concept can't be scaled to cover only the higher frequency bands to make them smaller. To get the low angle benefit from an overhead null, it is required only to have at least two wavelengths in the loop. Thus to make a long wire loop for, say, 10 meters, one could erect a one-wavelength loop cut for 20 meters. The formula for the length of wire required to make a one wavelength loop is:

$$L = 1005/f,$$

where L = length in feet, f = frequency in MHz. To make a long wire loop, simply double this amount. In this example, the long wire loop for 28.5 MHz would be only 70.5-ft in circumference, or about 23-ft on a side for a triangular shape. The point should also be made that although low angle enhancement does not occur for a one-wavelength loop, the Antenna is far from unusable. It is excellent for regional work and many swear by its overall performance. As another example, a one-wavelength loop cut for 80 meters is tour times smaller than the two-wavelength 160 meter loop, gives good regional performance on 80, and is still a long wire loop on 40 meters and up. As with all horizontal antennas, height is a virtue so the antenna should be mounted as high and in the clear as possible.

Conclusions: at Home on a Range

Long wire loop antennas have been shown to produce omnidirectional azimuth patterns free of the coverage nulls usually associated with long wire antennas through generation of complimentary vertical and horizontal polarization field components. If the loop is longer than one wavelength in circumference the vertically incident energy is suppressed, giving rise to a low takeoff angle for excellent DX performance. The overall average gain is about the same as an optimally oriented, resonant dipole cut for each band, but all at the same time, in all directions, and at a lower takeoff angle. As far as DX goes, it will not outperform an optimally pointed yagi mounted on a tall tower but it will provide solid performance in all directions, on all bands, and at a fraction of the cost.

Because a loop is resonant on all harmonics, the long wire loop can be used on all amateur bands from 160 through 10 meters with a modest antenna tuner and balanced teed with open wire line. The loop appears as a short at DC and has a low lightning profile compared to a tower, giving some measure of lightning protection. The combination of the DC short and harmonic resonant nature of the long wire loop minimizes out of band noise pickup, making the antenna very quiet on receive.

The shape of the loop affects the azimuth pattern and a triangular shape with a 40-degree apex angle at the feed point has been shown to produce particularly uniform azimuth patterns with a very low takeoff angle over many bands. Other shapes are possible and perhaps even better. If strict omnidirectionality isn't as important as expediency, the antenna can be tailored to fit in an existing space. The antenna lends well to modeling with NEC so the performance of a particular shape can be verified prior to construction. NEC and the user-friendly EZNEC embodiment by W7EL is a very effective method of predicting antenna performance without having to build and test the antenna on an antenna range. An additional attraction is the fact that the antenna is very low in cost, consisting of only wire and as few as three supports. On the downside, to cover the low frequency amateur bands the antenna has to be big. But if you've got the room or are just looking for something else to do with your ranch, this might be the antenna for you.

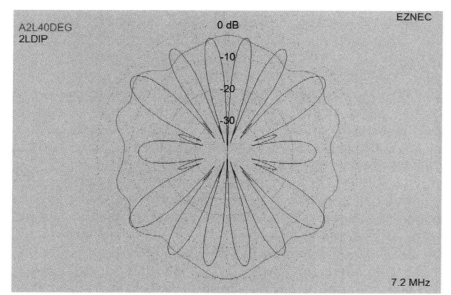

Figure I. Total Field Azimuth Pattern of A Long Wire Antenna and the Same Length Wire Folded into a Loop. The Long Wire Loop Provides Essentially Omnidirectional Performance with No Nulls.

The final platitude that can be ascribed to the long wire loop is multiband operation. Unlike a dipole, the loop resonates on all harmonics, not just the odd ones. The feed impedances arc "friendly", defined as not too high and non-reactive over a reasonable bandwidth. The actual impedance varies with harmonic order, installation height, and ground characteristics but generally is between 35 and 200 ohms, an easy target for any antenna tuner. Figure 4 shows a swept VSWR plot of a long wire loop for 80 meters (one wavelength on 160 meters). The harmonic resonant structure that serves every amateur band to 10 meters is clearly evident. From a practical standpoint, the antenna should be fed with open wire (ladder) line and a suitable tuner with balanced outputs.

(There is a full set of graphs available on Microsoft Powerpoint for your interest. Just email us for access. If we haven't convinced you with WA5FRF's story, these will win you over!)

Performance vs Shape: The Proof is in the Patterns

Tradeoffs in pattern and structural complexity exist regarding the actual shape of the long wire loop. Something can be said for enclosing as much area as possible for a given length of wire, and for this criterion, nothing beats a circle. However a true circle would take an infinite number of supports, and erecting such a structure would strain the bank and vacation balance accounts of even the most ardent amateur. Besides, as harmonic order increases, the azimuth pattern changes as a function of loop shape and some are better than others. Thanks to the magnificent EZNEC by Roy Lewallen W7EL, prediction of the patterns is, well, EZ. Figure 5 shows the total field azimuth patterns of octagonal, hexagonal, square, and triangular loops of one wavelength circumference on 160 meters at an installed height of 50-ft over average ground for the 160, 80, 60, 40, 20 and 10 meter amateur bands. Because of the foresight of the harmonic nature of the amateur frequency allocations, the antenna also works on the 30, 17, and 12 meter WARC bands but these were omitted to keep the figure a reasonable size. And yes, 60 meters isn't here yet, but one must have faith and it never hurts to plan ahead. As evidenced by the patterns, the triangular loop does a better job holding omnidirectionality across all bands. The square shape shows the most pattern lumpiness. These antennas would require respectively 8, 6, 4, and 3 supports and 546-ft of wire. To get a feel for the required real estate, the nearly circular octagonal loop would be about 173-ft in diameter and the triangular loop would be 181-ft on a side. A 3/4-acre square patch of land would be required to erect the antenna.

But the conversion from cloud warmer to barn burner doesn't happen until there are at least two wavelengths in the loop. To get the low angle benefit on the top band, the antenna has to be twice as big, requiring 1092-ft of wire and placing the fundamental resonance near 925 kHz. Figure 6 shows this data. The triangular shape again produces the most uniform patterns. The antenna would fit on a mere 3-acre square lot.

Because the triangular shape does well in producing omnidirectional patterns and requires only three supports, it is worthy of further study. Since the azimuth pattern is the superposition of fields from the three legs it can be modified by changes in the geometry and, in particular, the value of the apex angle at the corner containing the feed point. At some angle/frequency combinations, the antenna begins to take On the characteristics of a V-beam, producing 'pronounced forward gain in the pattern. Since the objective of this study is to identify loop shapes that produce omnidirectional coverage, these combinations are less desirable than those producing more or less equal radiation in all directions. Figures 7 and 8 shows the horizontal patterns by band for one and two wavelength loops (at 160 meters) for apex angles of 40, 50, 70, and 80 degrees. This represents a dither in the apex of the isosceles triangle loops of Figures 5 and 6 by +/-10 and +7-20 degrees. In all cases the total circumference remains the same. For the one wavelength series, the 50-degree triangle seems to exhibit the least amount of gain variation in azimuth. But for the two wavelength series, the 40-degree apex is clearly superior on the 160 through 40-meter bands. Dimensionally, this antenna is 407-ft long on each of the sides containing the feed point, 278-ft across the opposite side, and 50-ft above the ground. Sonic peaking is evident in many of the plots. If you have a preferred direction (like towards Europe) and have the option, you might as well orient the antenna accordingly.

Some of the magic begins to fade by 20 meters with the appearance of sonic peaks and valleys but the 20 and 10 meter patterns are far from unusable. To show just how well this antenna performs, Figure 9 compares the horizontal and vertical patterns of the two wavelength 40-degree triangular loop and a 160-meter dipole by band. When the dipole is harmonically operated, the patterns fall apart both in azimuth and elevation. By contrast, the long wire loop maintains significant omnidirectionality and the takeoff angle just keeps getting lower and more effective as harmonic order is increased.

In all of the azimuth patterns presented in the figures, the elevation angle was chosen either as an appropriate takeoff angle for the band or to include the highest gain of the antenna. The following table shows what these angles were for each band. In the case of the 160m dipole reference, the azimuth angle for the corresponding elevation plot also was chosen to reflect the best response.

Band	Elevation Angle
160m	45 deg
80m	35 deg
60m	35 deg
40m	22-32 deg
20m	13-20 deg
10m	8-10 deg

These elevation angles merit further comment. The long wire loop has a lower radiation angle than a dipole or even a three-element beam erected at the same height (50-ft). Only an antenna that actively suppresses vertical radiation can accomplish this feat.

An examination of the figures reveals that the average azimuth gain of the long wire loop is around +5dBi. This is very comparable to that obtained in the peak response of a resonant dipole cut for each band and mounted at the same height over the same ground type. Thus, operationally, using a long wire loop is like having a separate rotatable dipole for each band, always pointed towards the station you are working but with a lower takeoff angle"

There is a full set of graphs available on **Microsoft Powerpoint** for your interest. Just email The Wireman for access <orders@thewireman.com>. If we haven't convinced you with this story, these prints will win you over!

Our sincere thanks to Steve Cerwin, WA5FRF, for his permission for us to share this remarkable study with the readers of WIREBOOK V.

How about Stealth Antennas?

A very welcome story from a great "Elmer" in California last year, then 99 years old and a Ham for 72 of them! He is W6NKT, Harry K Wolf, and has been helping fellow hams build antennas at challenging QTH's for years. Here he describes his own wire dipole solution:

"You may be interested in my wire antenna. First of all – my lot is only twenty-five feet wide and the City said that I had to leave three feet of walkway on each side of the house. So my house is only 19 feet wide. My station is on the third floor and I have about eight feet of coax that goes from my antenna tuner through a wall to a storeroom where a 4;1 balun is located. On the storeroom floor there is about 12-15 feet of the 300 ohm twin lead that goes out the back of the center of the house to an insulator outside. This insulator is nine feet from each side of the house and is the feed point to each side of a dipole. The wire legs each run 55-59 feet along the back of the house to and through feed through insulators through rafters creating a wrap-around the house dipole of some 110 to 118 feet.

I have helped many Hams put up wire antennas that did not fit the dimensions of the books on antennas. All that I've said is 'Put it up and try it out'. In nearly every case the antennas did what they wanted."

This is a perfect example of the many "stealth" antennas we have helped Hams create – with tiny wire under the eaves, inside fiber glass flagpoles, dual duty clotheslines and dog runs, under shingles on the roof, as copper flashing on roofs, copper downspouts, even copper gutter loops around whole dwellings separated at the feed point with a plastic section, weather vanes, patio railings, and more. Where there's a will, there's a way!!

****

HORIZONTAL LOOP ANTENNA
Vernon Lee Gibbs, W4JTL

"In my 60 plus years of Amateur Radio I have tried almost all types of antennas. Some have been good performers and some have been more or less cloud warmers. You name it and I have tried it one time or another. And, since I am now 85 years of age and crippled up a bit, I have decided to quit climbing towers for safety sake, my safety that is. I wanted to come up with an antenna that can be raised and lowered by ropes and pulleys, work DX as well as locals—and discriminate against man-made noise[i]

It took me several years to understand that antenna *efficiency* is what counts, you don't see much written in articles about antenna efficiency. We are accustomed to expressing gain of an antenna in decibels, but db gain is a long way from the final criteria of how good an antenna really is. Because we often overlook *exactly how much power is used up in heat to get that "apparent" db gain.* Antenna efficiency is best described as a *ratio of the power radiated to the power lost.* We are talking about the power you can get out of an antenna with respect to the power you put into it.

When you are transmitting, the power supplied to the antenna, less the resistance losses, is radiated whether it is an antenna for two-meters or eighty-meters. But there is another type of efficiency called capture area or pick-up efficiency. The two-meter half wave antenna does not have the pick-up efficiency as the one for eighty-meters. An eighty-meter half-wave antenna picks up something like 2500 times more energy than the two-meter half-wave dipole. As an example, what would you rather be holding during a lightning storm—a two-meter rubber duck or the feed-line to a 134 foot antenna. That's capture area.

Before I decided on an antenna, I read several articles on various types and different configurations including Quads and Horizontal Loop Antennas[ii]. Jim Williams, N8IBR said, "I have been using a loop since I first read about them in Dave Fischer's Nov 1985 QST article, and can attest to the antennas excellent performance." Kirk A. Kleinschmidt, NT0D had this to say, "In my experience the best all-around multiband antenna is the horizontal loop." Then there is this statement by Paul D. Carr, N4PC who said, "Very few antennas in recent years have created as much controversy as the full-wave loop based on Dave Fischer's article in QST, ("The Loop Skywire, "Nov 1985)

In the last few years there have been very few antennas that have created as much excitement as the full-wave Horizontal Loop unless it was the famous G5RV antenna[iii] developed by R. L. Varney. But first we need to look at what it takes to make a good antenna. It's not really gain, nor is it one that produces a great radiation pattern. To put it in very simple terms, the most important thing with regard to any antenna is *efficiency.* That is why the old faithful center fed dipole made of wire, with open wire feeders, is still in use, and *sometimes* does as good a job as the beams up on high towers. And the dipole is still used today as a *reference* antenna.

Now let's take a look at an example of what antenna efficiency really is. The impedance of a resonant dipole at least one-half wavelength above earth is in the order of 70 ohms. *Impedance of an antenna is simply equal to the voltage applied to its terminals divided by the current flowing into those terminals.*

#12 copper wire has a resistance of 2 ohms per 1000 ft. A dipole cut for 80 meters is about 134 ft long. That equals about **a quarter ohm dc resistance**. But there are some ohmic *losses* introduced by surrounding objects, the poles or towers used to hold the antenna up, gutters on your house and out buildings, electrical and telephone lines, even the ground itself must be taken into account. So 134 feet of wire, when strung up as a dipole *usually* has about

2 ohms resistance. That is if all connections are tight and soldered.

Radiation resistance is the ohmic losses subtracted from the overall impedance. For example, 2 ohms subtracted from 70 ohms, leaves us 68 ohms. 68 ohms divided by 70 ohms = 97% efficiency. This means that our dipole is a 97 percent efficient radiator. If we put in 100 watts we loose only 3 watts as heat. The remainder of the 97 watts gets us that S9 report in Kenesia. **Now that is good efficiency**, in fact, the half wave dipole made from #12 copper wire, fed with open wire line made of #12 copper wire **is one of the most efficient antennas ever invented.** The higher the radiation resistance of the antenna **in relation to ohmic resistance**, the more efficient the antenna is going to be. This is true simply because the ratio of **good power** to **lost power** is high.

The laws of physics that govern antenna engineering today is the same as it was in the 30's, there is very little new technology. Dipoles have **always been** and will **continue to be** the all-around most popular and most used antennas.[iv]

So some will say a dipole has a gain of 2 db over an isotropic antenna. I think that is just foolishness. Antennas do not have any gain. They concentrate the power into a much narrower radiation pattern, that's all. Antennas are not amplifiers, for example, if you put 100 watts into an antenna that is all that you will ever get out of the antenna, even if it's a sterba curtain or a rhombic. All you can do is manipulate the pattern to get more of your 100 watts in one direction at the expense of less power in another direction. Antennas are not magic.[v]

Also the shorter we make an antenna physically, as in the case of the trapped beam, the lower the impedance goes. Some trap beams have an impedance of only 4 or 5 ohms. Some mobile antennas with 8 ft or less whips have an impedance of only 1 or 2 ohms, and the ohmic resistance is high. So you know what the efficiency is there.

Getting back to my antenna—I was still trying to decide what antenna to put up. I wanted one that would not have to be rotated, one that would have fairly low angle radiation, omni-directional, and not too susceptible to man-made noise. And one that would work all ham bands from 80 meters up. A pretty good order.

I said that the dipole made of copper wire was probably the most efficient antenna ever invented. That's true, **and** the Quad and Horizontal Loop antenna made of copper wire is also just as efficient a performer because the impedance is on the order of 120 ohms and the ohmic resistance is low. The Horizontal Loop is nothing more than a Quad radiator placed in the horizontal position. And the horizontal loop is not new. I remember a ham in the 70's who tied his gutters together on his four story apartment house and used it as a horizontal loop.

It seems that **all** of the users of the Horizontal Loops have nothing but praise for the performance in working both local's and DX, and eliminating much man-made noise.

The G5RV[vi], although really just a center fed dipole, is a good antenna. Varney used a matching section of ladder line to get 72 ohms. He could just as well have used ladder line all the way and tuned it with a Transmatch or something.

Here's another thing to consider. With a horizontal loop cut for resonance on 80 meters, the major vertical radiation lobe is straight up—**but** the higher in frequency you go the lower the vertical radiation lobe goes. For example, the 80 meter Horizontal Loop up 40 feet has a vertical angle of 90 degrees at the design frequency; 45 degrees on 40 meters, 35 degrees at 30 meters, 22 degrees on 20 meters, and a whopping low 11 degrees on the 10 meter band.

Doug DeMaw[vii], W1FB said that loops are known for being less responsive to man-made noise than are the other types of antennas. Since our power company erected a sub-station less than 350 feet from my residence, I needed an antenna that would discriminate against man-made noise.

Finally after all my research I decided to use the horizontal loop. And while I was at the Hamvention in Dayton, I contacted the Wireman[viii], got some good information from him, and purchased the necessary wire, ladder line, insulators, balun, nylon rope and pulleys.

According to Dave Fischer, the two fundamental requirements for the "Loop Skywire", which was what he called his horizontal loop, is its true horizontal position with respect to the earth below it, and the maximum enclosed area. The greater the enclosed area of the loop the better the performance will be. I installed my loop with each leg being of equal length and at the same height above ground.

And that is great for stateside contacts out to a thousand or so miles. But, according to Doug DeMaw, you can get results on the bands higher than 80 meters that are equal to or better than a three element tri-band Yagi up 65 feet.

Construction of the horizontal loop is simple. I placed marine pulleys[ix] at the top section of the four Rohn towers to raise and lower the antenna as shown in figure 1. I locked and tied an insulator in place at one corner and used corner-feed with ladder line as in figure 2. Later I will probably exchange the ladder line for open wire feeders. I floated the other three corners by placing the pulleys *on the loop wire as shown in figure 3* so that I could locate each of them at the three remaining corners. This allowed me to pull the slack out of the loop. I used pulleys *on the loop wire* and I put an insulator between them and the pulley that was used to pull the antenna up into place.

Because of the size and height of the horizontal loop, and with its *large capture area,* not only is it an excellent receiving antenna, it is an excellent target for lightning and static electricity. If you decide to erect a horizontal loop, I would suggest that you make provisions to easily disconnect the antenna from your equipment and ground it when not in use[x]

Put up a one wavelength horizontal loop for 160 meters, make it at least 40 feet high, feed it with open wire line and you will have an antenna that is hard to beat. But if you cannot get up one for 160 then go for 80 meters. The first thing you should do is determine the highest band you will be using and the frequency range you want the antenna to be resonant on. For example, if you are a CW operator, and you are an Extra Class, you will probably want to select the low end of the 10 meter band, say 28,012. Divide the 28012 by 8 and you get 3.5015 Mc., divide that into 1005 and you will get 287 feet. Divide that by 4 and you get 71'8", which will be the length of each side of the loop.

Paul Carr, N4PC, **(famous loop experimenter)** did considerable research before he erected *his* horizontal loop and he made this statement, *talking about his search for the ideal antenna* ; "If you place a blind hog under an oak tree, it will eventually find an acorn." *He said making reference to his Horizontal Loop:* **I think I have found my acorn.** Since I erected my horizontal loop I have been able to work almost all that I can hear and I have found that I can hear anyone that other stations in my area are working. I don't believe you could ask for more than that. My man-made noise level has dropped from an S3 to zero. The Horizontal Loop is a great receiving antenna. Doug DeMaw, W1FB, said in his article on Horizontal Loop Antennas; *the improvement in noise rejection during receive may be sufficiently rewarding to justify installing a horizontal loop. This is especially true if you live in a noisy neighborhood.* "

[i] Vernon Lee Gibbs, W4JTL, "Power Line Interference," WorldRadio Oct 2000

[ii] Dave Fischer, W0MHS, "The Loop Skywire," QST Nov 1985
Lew Ozimek, N2OZ, "The Full-Wave Loop Sky-Wire Antenna," CQ Feb 1977
Paul D. Carr, N4PC, "The N4PC Loop Antenna," CQ Dec 1990 and CQ Aug 1990
The ARRL Handbook, 16th and 19th Editions
Doug DeMaw, W1FB, "A Closer Look at Horizontal Loop Antennas," QST May 1990
Jim Williams, N8IBR, "On Loops" QST Correspondence, Sept 2002
John S. Belrose, VE2CV, "Loops for 80 Meter DX," QEX Aug 1997; A Horiz Loop for 80 Meter DX, QST Aug 2000
R.W. Stroud, "A Large Remote Tuned Loop for HF DX," CQ Jul 2001
E.A. Andress, W6KUT, A K6STI Low Noise Receiving Antenna, QST Sep 1995
Kirk Kleinschmidt, NT0Z, "A Balanced Everyday Approach to All Band Bliss," QST Apr 2002

[iii] G5RV, R.L. Varney, 3/2 wave antenna for 14mc

[iv] Dave Ingram, K4TWJ; CQ Nov 2002, "Straight Talk on Reduced-Size Antennas: A Basic Study

[v] AntennasWest 95

[vi] Building & Installing G5RV Anetnnas for Effective Multiband Performance, TechNote #124d, AntennasWest

[vii] Lew McCoy, W1ICP, "Antenna Efficiency—What is it?" CQ Apr 1995

[viii] The Wireman, Inc., Press Jones N8UG.

ix   Radio Works Stainless Steel Pulley #292

x   Vernon Lee Gibbs, W4JTL, "Lightning protection for the amateur station," WorldRadio Dec 2000

****

Our thanks to World Radio for permission to share W4JTL's great story here with you.

Time for the next (and last) quiz! Another easy True or False

Hard-drawn copper wire has higher break strength than that of soft-drawn copper wire of the same alloy or purity.
T/F

All copper clad steel wire is the same and makes a short lived antenna.
T/F

Stranded and solid wire of the same basic material will perform equally in equal life spans.
T/F

A dipole performs significantly better propagation-wise with a balun at the feed point.
T/F

Jacketed antenna wire will not perform as well as bare wire, all else being the same.
T/F

Answers at bottom of page 206

The Automotive red and black "zip" cord with heavy PVC jacket and 2 stranded bare copper conductors is a necessity for mobile radio installations. Here's the dope you need for making the right choices.

WM p/n	Wire Size (AWG)	Resistance per 1000 ft of each conductor	Maximum ft per Amp for 1 volt drop
341	6	0.63	1587
342	10	1	1000
343	12	1.59	629
344	14	2.52	397
345	16	4.02	249
346	18	6.39	156

Select the appropriate size based on the length you need and the total amperage required. Divide the amperage into a factor from the last column and compare the length you need. Twice your design length would allow a voltage drop of about 1/2 volt under full load.

A typical example: The DC line in the shack to a 50 watt transceiver divided by 13.6 VDC = 3.62 amps. For an 18 AWG line, divide 156 by 3.62 to learn that a 43 foot piece of 18 AWG zip cord would have a 1 volt drop, so if a 20 foot run from the battery in your vehicle was used, the voltage drop would be less than ½ volt, if the engine was running.

In your parked car, the fully charged battery supplies a little more than 12 VDC, so 50/3.62 = 4.17, and 156/4.17=37.4 feet for a 1 volt drop.

So, if you move up to 16 AWG, the same 4.17 into 249 = about 60 feet making your 20 footer dropping only 1/3 volt – hardly discernable unless you rag chew for hours!.

Last quiz answers: All false!